BOOK 3

THE COMPLETE SINGING RESOURCE FOR PRIMARY SCHOOLS

Val Whitlock & Shirley Court

Boosey & Hawkes Music Publishers Ltd
www.boosey.com

Acknowledgements

The Nursery Rhyme Rap, *Kapulu Kane* and *Animals Live in the Forest* from B Joan E Haines & Linda L Gerber *Leading Young Children to Music*, 6th Edition. Published by Allyn and Bacon/Merrill Education, Boston MA. Copyright © 1996 by Pearson Education. Reprinted and recorded by permission of the publisher
Did You Feed My Cow? adaptation of music, words and some new words Ella Jenkins. Ell-Bern Publishing Co, 1844 N Mohawk St, Chicago, Illinois 60614
Geppetto Made a Puppet, *Pinocchio* and *Down, Down to the Bottom of the Sea* copyright © 2009 by Faber Music Limited. Printed by permission
Words to *The Engine Driver* reproduced by permission of Lindell Green
The Little Pigs' Jive © copyright 1986 by Linda L Gerber and B Joan E Haines
All other works © copyright 2009 Boosey & Hawkes Music Publishers Ltd

Publisher's note
The publishers have used their best efforts to clear the copyright works included in this book with the relevant owners and to print suitable acknowledgments. If any right owner has not been consulted or an acknowledgement omitted, the publishers offer their apologies and will rectify the situation following formal notification.

Piano accompaniments to *Toes A-Twinklin', Eat Me!, Sherlock's Sports Day, Make Friends Around the World, My Birthday Party,* and *Wannabe* by Ashley Thompson

Recording credits
Singers: Modinat Adekunle, Jon Laird, Emma Shearmur, Rachael Somers, Val Whitlock (directed by Val Whitlock) and the pupils of Lower Peover Primary School, Cheshire, with Nicola Howbrigg (directed by Shirley Court). With special thanks to the Head Teacher and staff of the school.

CDs arranged and produced by Andrew Holdsworth, Method and Madness Music

Published by Boosey & Hawkes Music Publishers Ltd
Aldwych House
71–91 Aldwych
London
WC2B 4HN

www.boosey.com

ISMN 979-0-060-11876-0
ISBN 978-0-85162-513-3

Second impression 2012

Printed in England by The Halstan Printing Group Ltd, Amersham, Bucks

Notesetting by The Note Factory

Illustrations by Paul Russell

Foreword

The *Singing Sherlock* series is a firm favourite of singing leaders throughout the land and deservedly too. I have seen Val Whitlock and Shirley Court demonstrating their captivating skills with Key Stage 2 and 3 young singers on many occasions and so I am particularly delighted to see that they have now focused their expertise on the 'starter' generation of even younger singers. After all, if the foundations of a building are not properly laid, it is more likely to come tumbling down at a later stage!

They know their stuff and they know that some teachers will feel confident in leading their young singers while others – probably the majority – are scared of taking the plunge. What makes *Singing Sherlock* such a valuable resource is that it gives every possible encouragement and support to the latter group with hands-on, tried and tested tips, clues and tricks.

Best of all, there is a well-thought-through sense of progression in this volume from basic warm-up physical exercises such as 'standing tall like a giraffe' through to performing fully-fledged group songs with developed parts and musical stories. It won't just be the children who embark on this journey, either, as many adults will find this step-by-step approach very reassuring as they too gradually master the tools of the trade themselves. All of this is achieved whilst keeping the songs and games fun, funny, catchy and imaginative.

The *Singing Sherlock* series shares an ambitious and noble aspiration with our National Singing Programme, *Sing Up*, to enable the re-birth of all-class singing throughout the country: a whole generation of children are being given back something that should never have been lost in the first place – their right to sing together, to make music together, to discover their voices together. What an exciting time to be contributing to this re-awakening with new songs, techniques and ideas, as this collection does, helping children to 'stand tall like giraffes' and to fill the air with their joyful chorus.

Howard Goodall, composer & broadcaster
National Ambassador for Singing

Ideal for use with *Sing Up* and *Wider Opportunities* class singing programmes in the UK, *Singing Sherlock* also fits with DCFS/QCA Schemes of Work for Music – ongoing skills.

The Authors

Val Whitlock

Renowned for her infectious enthusiasm, energy and ability to motivate people about singing, Val currently pursues a busy freelance role combining various strands as a workshop leader, choral director, voice consultant, author and singer. She also works part-time for Solihull Music Service as a vocal and choral specialist.

As a choral and vocal animateur Val is experienced with all ages and abilities from nursery level through to adult and is in demand nationally to direct large-scale performances and choral events, often involving hundreds of young people. She is a highly sought-after vocal trainer to national music organisations, music services and universities; and frequently acts as a consultant for various national vocal initiatives. She is a regular mentor and presenter for *Music for Youth* and adjudicator for other choir festivals.

Val directs two very successful choirs for Solihull Music Service – *Songsquad*, and their training choir *The Rookies* – as well as acting as guest conductor for other youth choirs.

Val is a graduate in Performing Arts, and also studied voice as a post-graduate at the Birmingham Conservatoire of Music and with the Southbank Centre's *Voicelab PULSE*.

Shirley Court

Shirley is nationally known for her ability to motivate and inspire young singers of all ages and capabilities. In September 2006 she was awarded an Honorary DMus for her work with youth choirs and her contribution to music in schools by the University of Leicester.

She regularly conducts massed choirs of primary school children for various local authorities and also for events such as *Music for Youth's Schools' Prom* at the Royal Albert Hall. She is also a regular presenter of *Music for Youth's Primary Proms,* both in Birmingham and Chester.

Shirley was the conductor of both the Senior and Junior CBSO Youth Choruses from 1995 to 2009. In this capacity she has worked alongside world-famous conductors preparing the Youth Chorus for many prestigious events.

Currently Shirley works part-time for Cheshire Music Partnership as part of the Cheshire Vocal Strategy and the Cheshire Youth Choir – who gained a silver award at the 2008 Choral Olympics in Graz.

In September 2008 she was appointed Director of the Halle Children's Choir. Shirley also acts as a consultant on many national singing initiatives and runs many vocal inset courses for teachers.

Word sheets

Word sheets for all the songs in this book are available to download from:
www.boosey.com/resources

Contents

Singing Sherlock Investigates (page 2)

Warm-ups (page 6)

Section 1 – Feel The Heartbeat! (page 11)

Section 2 – Tune In! (page 31)

Section 3 – Sing the Story (page 52)

Section 4 – Sherlock in Concert (page 84)

Singing Sherlock investigates ...

... and solves the mystery of how to get children to sing well ...

Follow the clues ...

Hi! I'm
Singing Sherlock

- *I watch and listen to you carefully*
- *I ask questions to help you sing better*
- *Can you take a turn at being Singing Sherlock too?*

and check out the case notes ...

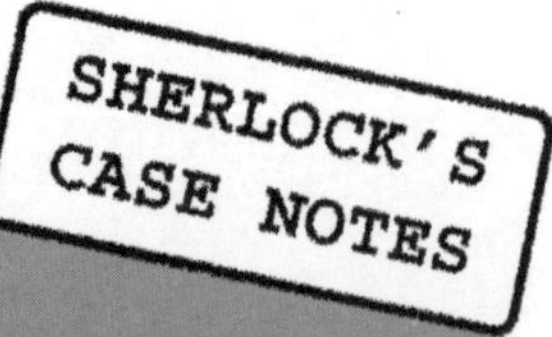
SHERLOCK'S
CASE NOTES

Investigate:

- *Background to the song*
- *How to teach the song*
- *What to expect from the children*
- *Points to look out for*

... but first ...

Do your groundwork!

Choose the right song

Songs should be chosen from *each* of the first three sections, rather than working through the book from the beginning to the end. Many of the songs are interchangeable between the first three sections, as the vocal demands and musical concepts explored within the songs will often overlap.

When planning a singing session choose a balance of songs, mixing a more difficult song with easier songs, and action songs with songs in other styles.

The songs in each section are grouped in *approximate* order of difficulty. However, the songs in the *Sing the Story* section and *Sherlock in Concert* are the most demanding, both musically and vocally.

Learn the song yourself

Do not attempt to teach the song before you know it well yourself. Prepare thoroughly – listen to the CD and sing along, play or sing using the music – whichever is most comfortable for you. Even if you do not plan to use the CD backing tracks in your singing session, listening to the CD will give you a good idea of how the songs should be performed.

A singing school is a happy school

Make singing a daily activity. Sing with your class, with several year groups together and sing with the whole school. It should be vibrant and fun but above all it should be quality singing. The better the *quality*, the more pleasurable and satisfying it will be for the children, the teacher and audience.

How you teach the song is really important!

PRIORITY

Set the scene

You need space to sing. Singing is a very physical activity, so children need space to move their bodies freely and without tension. Be aware that desks can act as a barrier, so it is worth moving these to the side of the room to create a singing area.

Vary the amount of time the children sit or stand on the floor. A session might include standing or sitting in a circle, in a group or moving around. If the session includes a variety of vocal activities as well as movement the children will not notice how long they are on their feet.

Children need a good singing example

The best way to teach a song to children is by using your *own* voice. When they are learning to sing, children will pitch more accurately from a human voice than from any other instrument or CD track.

However, if you are not a confident singer you can use the backing CDs, but always remember children will respond to *your* enthusiasm. For some of the simpler songs, you could invite a child from upper Keystage 2 to be a singing buddy to help you lead, or if you are able to, enlist the help of another adult who is a more confident singer, even if only occasionally.

Always aim for a stimulating and positive environment where the energy level is high and the activities are interesting so that the children never lose interest or motivation. Remember small children have a short attention span – little and often is best.

Teaching the song by singing yourself

- Sing through the song, or a verse of the song, to show how it goes.
- Use a call and response method, *eg* sing a phrase and ask the children immediately to sing back. Add a phrase at a time, then put two phrases together and gradually build up the song.
- The children will memorise the songs more quickly this way and consequently will sing with more confidence and enjoyment. Always give them a digestible amount to sing back.
- If you feel confident, you can also show the shape of the melody with your hands as you sing. This is called *patterning*, and it can help the children see when the tune is going up or down, and help pinpoint any intervals between notes that the children find difficult.

- Maintain a good pace throughout the singing session, so that the children do not get bored and lose interest. Remember, talk less – sing more.
- Try not to sing when the children sing back a phrase so that you can listen for wrong notes or other insecurities.
- Always sort out any mistakes the children make *as they first happen*. Once faults have become established they are difficult and sometimes impossible to correct. Try singing the phrase again, or highlight the difficult passage using nonsense words like *Na na na* or *Doo doo doo*, or perhaps sing the phrase in a different kind of voice. If you make it humorous the children will catch on quickly.

Are you ready? Off we go!

- When teaching a song always remember to give a starting note, and count the children in. You may sing "1, 2, 3, 4" or "Are you ready? Off we go …" on the starting note. You could also use a recorder or a tuned instrument to sound the note.
- However you do it you need to indicate whether the song is in two, three or four time.
- The starting note and count in are stated at the beginning of each song in this book.

Using the CD to teach the song

- When using the CD to teach the song, do not be tempted merely to play the CD and ask the children to sing along in the hope that they will simply 'pick up' the tune. In practice what often happens is that many children can end up learning the tune, or sections of the tune, quite inaccurately and these mistakes will be almost impossible to correct afterwards.
- Play through the song once, so that the children hear how it goes.
- Next, play through the song again, but this time ask the children to join in with any repeated parts of the song or any simple actions.
- Continue in this way, putting the song together by learning short sections until it is completely familiar to the children.
- It is important that the children can hear themselves when they sing, so be careful not to allow the CD track to drown the children's voices.

Warm-ups

Energise your body

The larynx is part of the body's whole muscular system, and therefore the entire body should be involved in the process of singing. Just as athletes warm up their muscles before a race, singers need to warm up both the body and the vocal folds before singing. A good warm-up also helps get rid of any tension in the body so it should always be fun. Songs and warm-ups that involve actions help release the voice and focus attention.

Wobbly Jelly

Shake your body as if you are a wobbly jelly at a birthday party.

Ceiling Stretch

Stretch up high and try to touch the celing. Now reach down and touch the floor.

Fish Fingers

Be a wobbly jelly and when the teacher/leader calls "fish fingers" everyone freezes in whatever position they have ended up in. Remember, no defrosted fish fingers and certainly no giggling fish fingers!

Strike the right pose – good singing posture

Standing to sing

- Make sure that you have enough space between you and the next person.
- Can you stand tall like a giraffe?
- Make sure that your shoulders are down and give your arms a little shake.
- Pull your shoulders up to your ears then, as your drop them down, let out a whispered "wow" and look surprised and excited.

Sitting to sing

- Make sure that you have enough space between you and the next person.
- If you are sitting on chairs, make sure that there is enough space between your chair and the person sitting next to you.
- Always sit tall, even when sitting on the floor.
- Remember to keep your neck long like a giraffe.

Voice Stretch Activities

1. Jimbo Jambo

Jimbo jambo jiggle and jive,
Let's all dance and count to five.
(speaking voice) One two three four five!
(whispering voice) One two three four five!
(thinking voice) One two three four five!

Zibedee zebedee dance some more,
Feel the beat and count to four.
(speaking voice) One two three four!
(whispering voice) One two three four!
(thinking voice) One two three four!

(with a high voice) Whoop-si-doo wiggle your knees,
Swing your arms and count to three.
(speaking voice) One two three!
(whispering voice) One two three!
(thinking voice) One two three!

(with a twang like an American cowboy) Hi-dee hi and how d'ya do?
Stamp your feet and count to two!
(speaking voice) One two!
(whispering voice) One two!
(thinking voice) One two!

Diddley dum, we're down to one.
Let's sit down as we're all done!
PHEW!

Vocal Footsteps
Focus and energy
Internalising pulse (see pages 12–13 for an explanation of this concept)
Lips and tongue workout – developing the children's diction and stretching the range of the voice
Using different vocal qualities (for a detailed explanation of vocal qualities, particularly for older children, see Singing Sherlock Book 4.

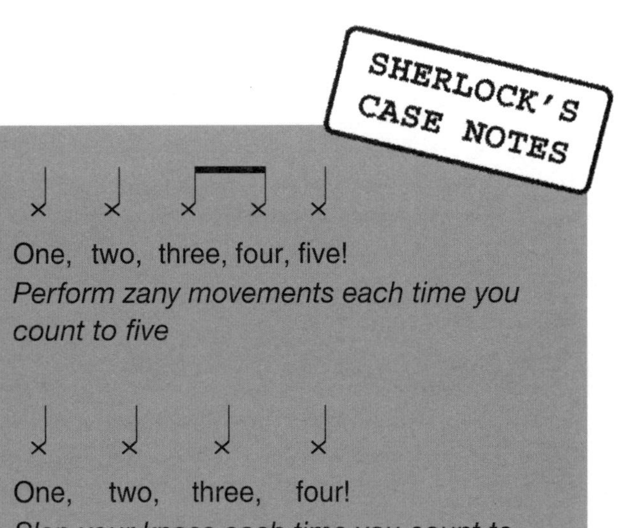

One, two, three, four, five!

- *Perform zany movements each time you count to five*

One, two, three, four!

- *Slap your knees each time you count to four*

One, two, three!

- *Swing your arms as if marching each time you count to three*

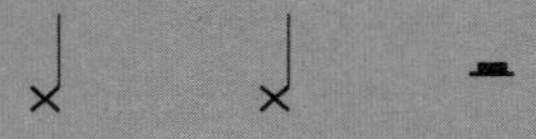

One, two!

- *Stamp your feet each time you count to two*

- *All sit down and mop your brows, looking totally exhausted*

- *To teach this warm-up, start by asking the children to echo repeated consonants, eg j j j j, m m m m, b b b b, g g g g, v v v v etc.*
- *Next teach them the first rhyme 'jimbo jambo jiggle and jive', making sure they are clearly sounding the consonants by working their lips and tongue.*
- *Check to see that the children are feeling the pulse as they perform the different movements to each verse. Do not forget the rests when chanting the numbers.*
- *When using their 'thinking' voices the children should hear the words, in time, in their heads without saying them. Initially they may find it easier to mime the words. Make sure the children do not whisper when using their 'thinking' voices.*

2. Singing Sherlock's a Real Cool Chap

Chant

All: Singing Sherlock's a real cool chap

(mime a singer) He likes to hear you sing

(clap on the word 'clap') And he likes to hear you clap

(use a high voice and point to the ceiling) He exercises voices so they stretch up high

(use a low voice and point to the floor) and low

(do a hand-jive on "off we go!") So come on everybody, off we go!

(use a whispering voice) **Teacher/leader:** "Let's try out our secret voice: I'm playing hide and seek."

Children: "I'm playing hide and seek."

Teacher: "Pretend you haven't seen me!"

Children: "Pretend you haven't seen me!"

Chant *(repeat)*

(use a posh voice) **Teacher/Leader:** "Let's try out our posh voice: Helleau."

Children: "Helleau."

Teacher: "I'm very pleased to meet you!"

(shake hands with your next-door neighbour) **Children:** "I'm very pleased to meet you!"

Continue in this way using the following:

(using a robot voice, mime being a Darlek) **Teacher/Leader:** "Let's try out our Dalek voice: Exterminate!"

(use a Bugs Bunny voice and mime rabbit ears) **Teacher/Leader:** "Let's try out our Bugs Bunny voice: nyer, wot's up doc? Got any carrots?"

(use a twangy voice and mime a flashing light with your hand) **Teacher/Leader:** "Let's try out our police car voice: nee-nar, nee-nar, nee-nar, nee-nar!"

(sing to a well known simple tune such as Twinkle Twinkle Little Star*)* **Teacher/Leader:** "Let's try our singing voice: hello everyone, are you singing well?"

Children: "Yes *(insert teacher's name)* we are singing well."

Use your own ideas!

Vocal Footsteps

- Focus and energy
- Awareness of high and low sounds
- Stretching the range of the voice
- Exploring different vocal qualities (see Sherlock's Case Notes)
- Using facial expressions to communicate the words

SHERLOCK'S CASE NOTES

- *First teach the children the chant making sure that all the words are really clear.*
- *Ask the children to pretend to be each of the characters as well as using their voices in different ways.*
- *You could also ask smaller groups, trios, pairs or a soloist to perform the responses.*
- ***NB** For a more detailed explanation of vocal qualities, particularly for older children, see* Singing Sherlock Book 4.

3. Wesley Bear's Day at the Office

One day Wesley Bear arrived at work. He got out of his bearmobile and walked to the office block:

Pd, pd, pd, pd, pd, pd, pd, pd *(do walking actions using two fingers)*

Wesley Bear arrived at the lift.

He pressed the button to open the door: Ping! *(make a lift bell sound)*

Up in the lift to the very top floor:

Oooo *(make a low to high sound)* Ping!

Wesley Bear walked to his desk:

Pd, pd, pd, pd, pd, pd, pd, pd

He opened his bearcase, but realised he had left his honey pot in the car:

Oh no! Shock horror! *(take a huge gulp of breath, bringing your hands to your face as you do so)*

He walked back to the lift:

Pd, pd, pd, pd, pd, pd, pd, pd

He pressed the button to open the door: Ping!

Down in the lift to the ground floor:

Oooo *(make a high to low sound)* Ping!

Wesley Bear walked to his bearmobile:

Pd, pd, pd, pd, pd, pd, pd, pd

He opened the bearmobile door: Click, click *(click with your tongue and mime pressing the car door key)*

He took out his honeypot, and walked back to the lift:

Pd, pd, pd, pd, pd, pd, pd, pd

He pressed the button to open the door: Ping!

Up in the lift to the very top floor:

Oooo ↗ Ping!

Wesley Bear walked back to his desk:

Pd, pd, pd, pd, pd, pd, pd, pd

He had just got back to his desk when he remembered he had forgotten to lock his car:

Oh no! Shock horror!

He walked back to the lift:

Pd, pd, pd, pd, pd, pd, pd, pd

He pressed the button to open the door: Ping!

Down in the lift to the ground floor:

Oooo ↘ Ping!

Wesley Bear walked to his bearmobile:

Pd, pd, pd, pd, pd, pd, pd, pd

He locked the bearmobile door: *Click, click*

He walked back to the lift:

Pd, pd, pd, pd, pd, pd, pd, pd

He pressed the button to open the door: Ping!

Up in the lift to the very top floor:

Oooo ↗ Ping!

He got back to his desk and realised he had left his laptop in the boot of the car:

Oh no! Shock horror!

He opened the window and put on his bunjee jumping equipment:

"No more lifts for me!",

shouted Wesley and jumped out of the window!

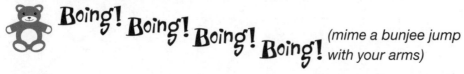

Boing! Boing! Boing! Boing! *(mime a bunjee jump with your arms)*

Vocal footsteps

- Stretching the range of the voice
- Using the voice creatively
- Using the voice expressively to tell a story
- Story sequencing

SHERLOCK'S CASE NOTES

- *Begin by introducing the different sounds and actions, eg walking Wesley Bear; lift PING!; key click; lift going up and down; shock horror; and bunjee jump.*
- *The teacher then reads the story and the children join in adding the sound effects and actions only.*
- *As the children become more familiar with the story they can then join in with the repeated phrases, ie "He pressed the button to open the door" and "Up in the lift to the very top floor" – shown in bold.*

Section 1 – Feel The Heartbeat

Clues to pulse and rhythm

The ability to internalise a pulse is essential for any kind of music making – both playing an instrument and singing. Children also need to be able to distinguish between pulse and rhythm. (See *Singing Sherlock Book 1* for a fuller explanation of the concepts of pulse and rhythm, plus associated activities.) All the songs in this section give children opportunities to respond physically – by moving and dancing – to rhythmic rhymes, chants and circle games with a strong pulse.

Pulse 

- Children may find it easier to move their bodies first before *patsching* (slapping knees) or clapping the pulse. Swaying, swinging arms, doing a jive or shaking a partner's hand in time really get the pulse into the body. Be aware however, that very small children can find marching in time to music quite difficult.

- Never be tempted to take hold of a child's hand to help them clap or patsch knees in time – they will merely stiffen up. Instead gently tap on their shoulders so they can *feel* the pulse in their body.

- Tap the pulse on a drum or tambour and ask the children to listen carefully and match their body movements or patsching to the sound of the drumbeat.

- When asking children to sing and move, or chant and move at the same time, do not be surprised if the singing initially suffers. Make sure the children practise both elements separately until they are really confident before combining them.

Rhythm ♫

- Always start by clapping or tapping short, simple phrases such as a child's name, or one line from a simple rhyme.
- When clapping simple rhythmic phrases, ensure the children make a sound for each syllable of the word, *eg*

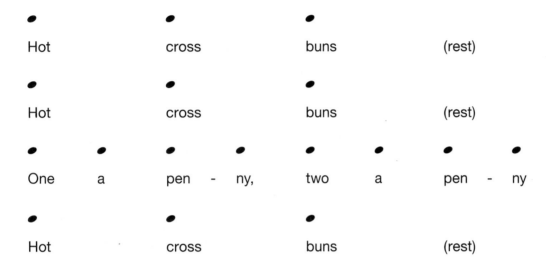

Hot		cross		buns		(rest)	
Hot		cross		buns		(rest)	
One	a	pen -	ny,	two	a	pen -	ny
Hot		cross		buns		(rest)	

- Ask the children to speak and sing the words aloud as they clap. Where appropriate, ask the children to make an 'open hand' movement to indicate the rest in the music.
- Next ask the children to mime the words and use their thinking voices (hear the words in their heads) whilst still clapping. Again, never be tempted to take hold of their hands – gently tap the rhythm on their shoulders so they can feel it through their body.
- The ability to hold a rhythm over an underlying pulse is a more demanding skill that takes time to assimilate. With older KS1 children ask half the class to patsch the pulse while the other half claps the rhythm of a known song or rhyme, *eg*

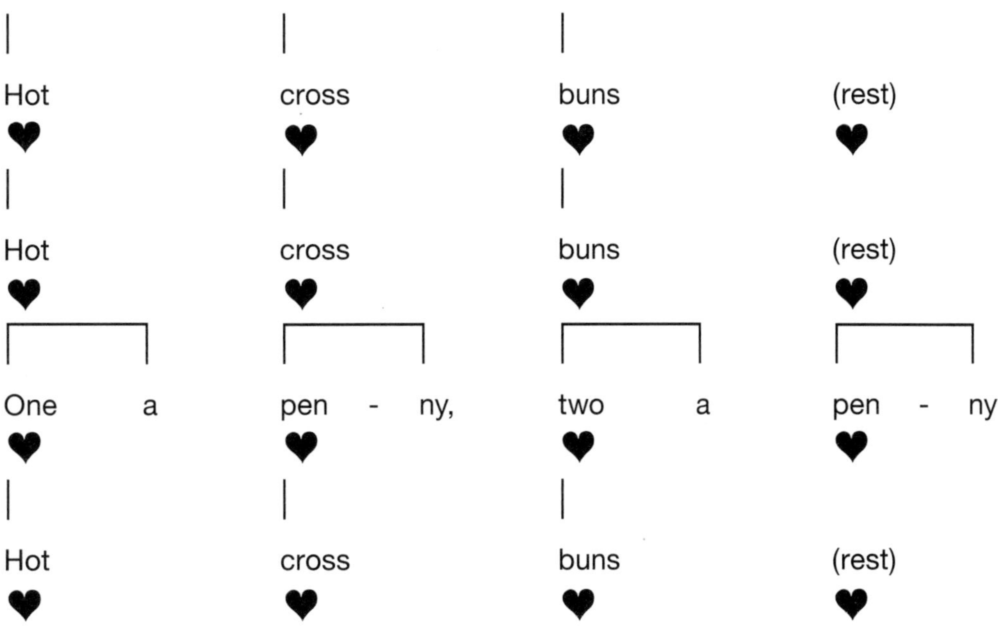
Hot cross buns (rest)
Hot cross buns (rest)
One a pen - ny, two a pen - ny
Hot cross buns (rest)

The Nursery Rhyme Rap

performance – CD 1 track 1; backing – CD 1 track 2
no starting note (chorus is rapped); introduction – 8 beats

Mark Weeks

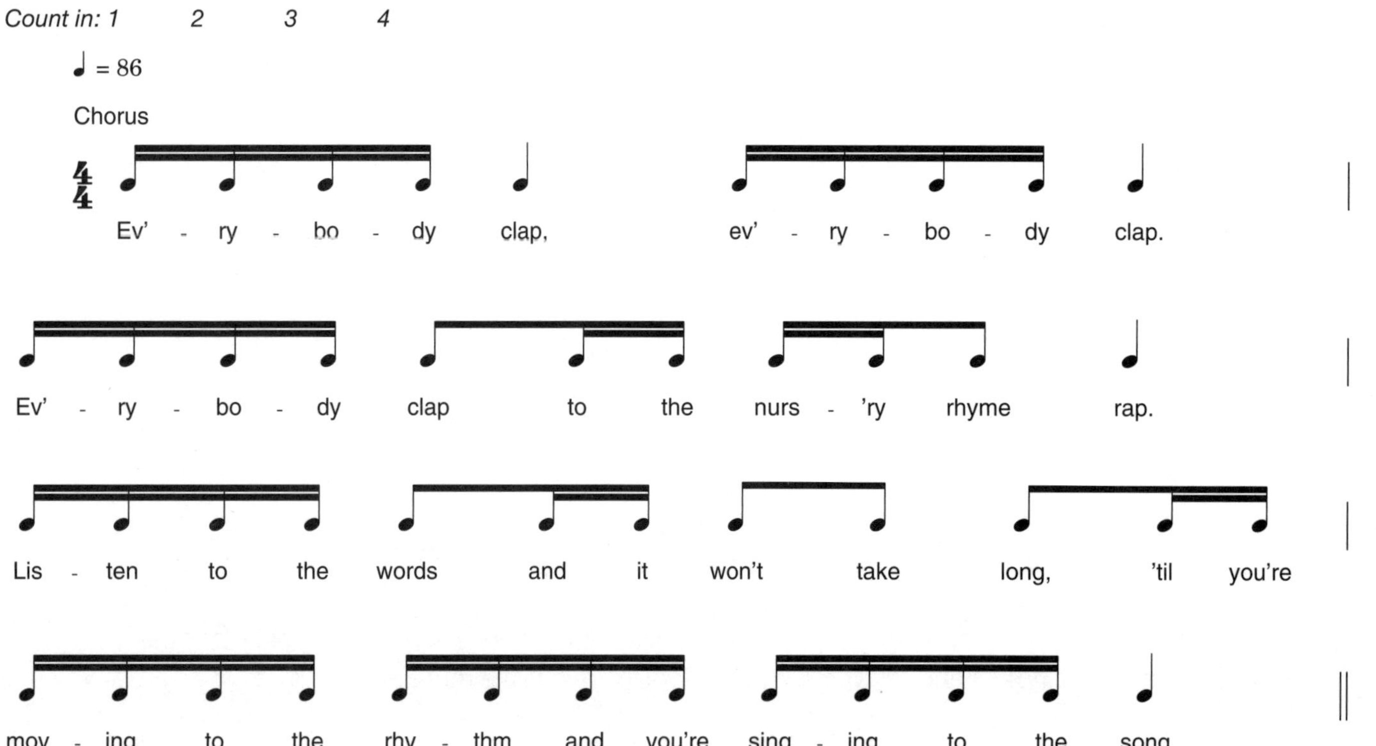

Ev' - ry - bo - dy clap, ev' - ry - bo - dy clap.
Ev' - ry - bo - dy clap to the nurs - 'ry rhyme rap.
Lis - ten to the words and it won't take long, 'til you're
mov - ing to the rhy - thm and you're sing - ing to the song.

1. 1, 2, 3, 4, 5, once I caught a fish alive,
   6, 7, 8, 9, 10, then I let it go again.
   Why did you let it go?
   Because it bit my finger so.
   Which finger did it bite?
   This little finger on the right.

   Chorus

2. Polly put the kettle on,
   Polly put the kettle on,
   Polly put the kettle on,
   We'll all have tea.

   Sukey take it off again,
   Sukey take it off again,
   Sukey take it off again,
   They've all gone away.

   Chorus

3. Hot cross buns,
   Hot cross buns,
   One a-penny, two a-penny,
   Hot cross buns.

   If you have no daughters,
   Give them to your sons,
   One a-penny, two a-penny,
   Hot cross buns.

   Chorus

4. Mary, Mary quite contrary,
   How does your garden grow?

   With silver bells and cockle shells,
   And pretty maids all in a row.

   Chorus

- Are you keeping the pulse steady as well as keeping in time with each other?
- Can you tap the pulse on your partner's shoulder?
- Can you think of different ways to chant the chorus? For example, can you use your whispering voice or your talking voice?
- Are you listening carefully when the other groups of singers perform their nursery rhymes?

SHERLOCK'S CASE NOTES

- *Using rhythmic chants in young children's early musical experience is very important for developing their sense of pulse.*
- *For the youngest children it is probably enough that they initially chant the nursery rhymes rather than sing them. This gives them time to internalise the word rhythms and feel the pulse before attempting to sing the melodies of the rhymes.*
- *Add a rhythmic swing, patsch or clap to keep the pulse.*
- *Once the children have internalised the pulse you could use unpitched percussion instruments,* eg *rhythm sticks, or woodblocks. Add jingle sticks or bells for special effects, for example for the line "silver bells and cockle shells" in* Mary, Mary Quite Contrary.
- *Teach everyone the rap and all the nursery rhyme verses. When all the children are confident, divide the singers into different groups, with each group singing one of the nursery rhyme verses. Everyone then joins together in the rap chorus. If you have strong singers some of the verses could also be performed as solos.*

Toes A-Twinklin'

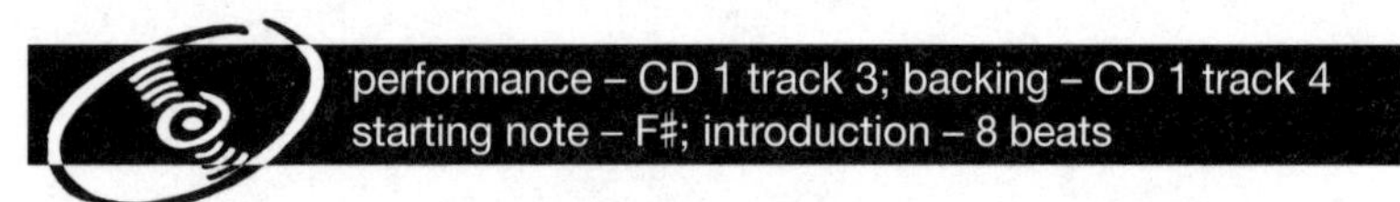
performance – CD 1 track 3; backing – CD 1 track 4
starting note – F♯; introduction – 8 beats

Sue Nicholls

Country & Western ♩ = 88
Count in: 1 2 3 4
N/C
D
D
Em
Here in Tex-as U - S - A,

last time to Coda
4
A
D
D
Em
A
D
folks go dan - cin' ev - 'ry day! When the ban-jo's play - in' sweet, click your heels and stamp your feet.

7
G
D
A
D
D7/F♯
G
D
Yee ha! Slap your thigh. Hands to your part - ner, don't be shy! Yee ha! Slap your thigh.

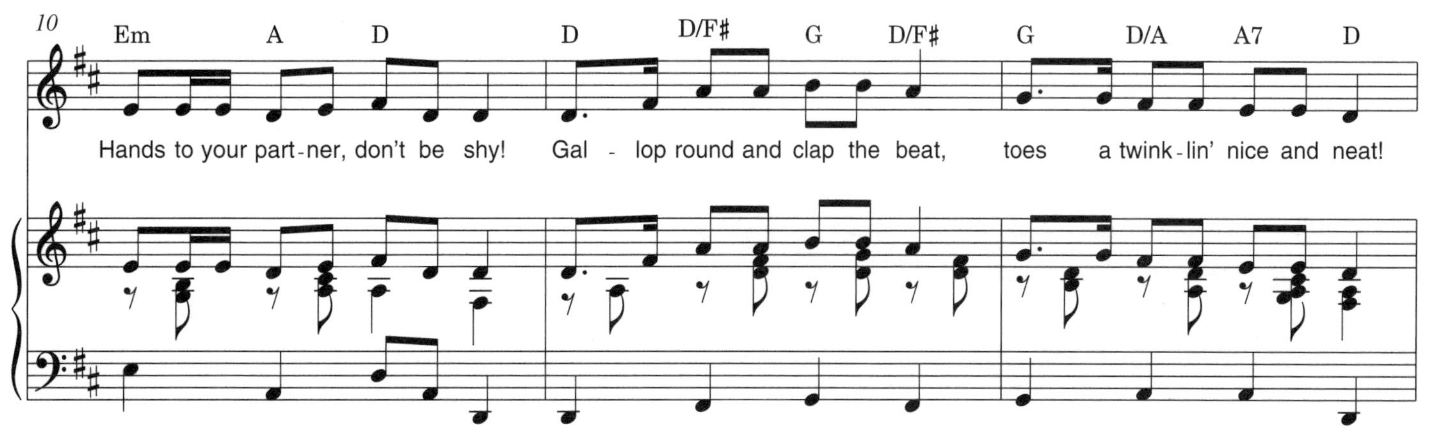

- Are your movements in time with the singing?
- Are you still singing whilst you gallop round?
- When the outer circle is galloping, is the inner circle clapping in time with the music?
- Are you ready, facing your new partner, on the words "wonder who you're gonna meet"?

SHERLOCK'S CASE NOTES

- *This is a Country & Western style circle dance.*
- *The children are arranged in two concentric circles, facing a partner.*
- *Do the following actions as you sing the lines:*

– "Here in Texas USA" – tuck your thumbs into imaginary braces and perform 'funky chicken' elbows. (You may have to explain what braces are, otherwise the children may think you are referring to braces on their teeth!)

– "When that banjo's playin' sweet" – mime strumming the banjo.

– "Click your heels and stamp your feet" – do exactly that!

– "Yee Ha" – punch your fists in the air twice then slap your thigh twice.

– "Gallop round and clap the beat" – the outer circle only gallops round while the inside circle claps on the beat.

– "Wonder who you're gonna meet?" – stand opposite your new partner.

The Little Pigs' Jive

Linda L Gerber and B Joan E Haines

Count in:

1 2 3 4

(spoken)
This is a story by Old Mother Goose,
About three little pigs who were out on the loose.

The first little pig built his house of straw –
The cutest little house that you ever saw.

And he huffed (*huff, huff*) and he puffed (*puff, puff*),
And the little pig ran to the second pig's place.

The second little pig built his house of sticks,
But the big bad wolf was up to his tricks.

Chorus

And he huffed (*huff, huff*) and he puffed (*puff, puff*),
And the little pig ran to the third pig's place.

The third little pig built his house of bricks.
They were stronger than straw, they were stronger than sticks.

Chorus

And he huffed (*huff, huff*) and he puffed (*puff, puff*),
And the little pig stayed in the third pig's place.

The big bad wolf said, "Let me come in,
Or I'll slide down the chimney and I'll do you in!"

C7aug F Gm7 B♭/C
"Come in, come in! We are read - y for you,
F B♭7 C7 F
And you nev - er will guess what we're go - ing to do!"
C7aug F F7 B♭ G7
And the three lit - tle pigs made the fire red - hot
C7 F
And they boiled up the wa - ter in the big ___ black pot!

And he slid (*swish, swish*)! Yes, he did (*swish, swish*)!
And he fell in the water in the middle of the night,
And the little pigs laughed because
IT SERVED HIM RIGHT!

Singing Sherlock wants to know:

- *Can you find a way to make your voice sound like the big bad wolf and use a different voice for the three little pigs?*
- *Are you managing to keep the slap-clap pulse in time with the rap?*
- *Can you feel your tummy muscles working on the huffs and the puffs?*

SHERLOCK'S CASE NOTES

- *The song can be performed with a slap–clap pulse.*
- *It will take several sessions to learn this song but the children should pick up the words quite quickly after a few repetitions.*
- *Divide the class into two halves, one to play the part of the big bad wolf and the other to play the part of the little pigs.*
- *The narrator's part could be performed by everyone or perhaps by a confident soloist.*

Eat Me!

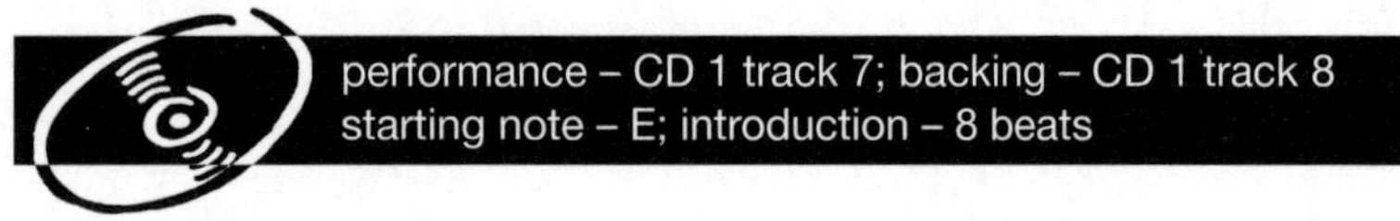
performance – CD 1 track 7; backing – CD 1 track 8
starting note – E; introduction – 8 beats

Sue Nicholls

With bounce ♩ = 142
Count in: 1 2 3 4
C C/E F G Em Am7 G C C C/E
Veg and fruit, it's

6
F G Em Am7 Dm7 G F C F C
heal-thy stuff! Do we real - ly eat e - nough? Five bits dai - ly, may-be more?

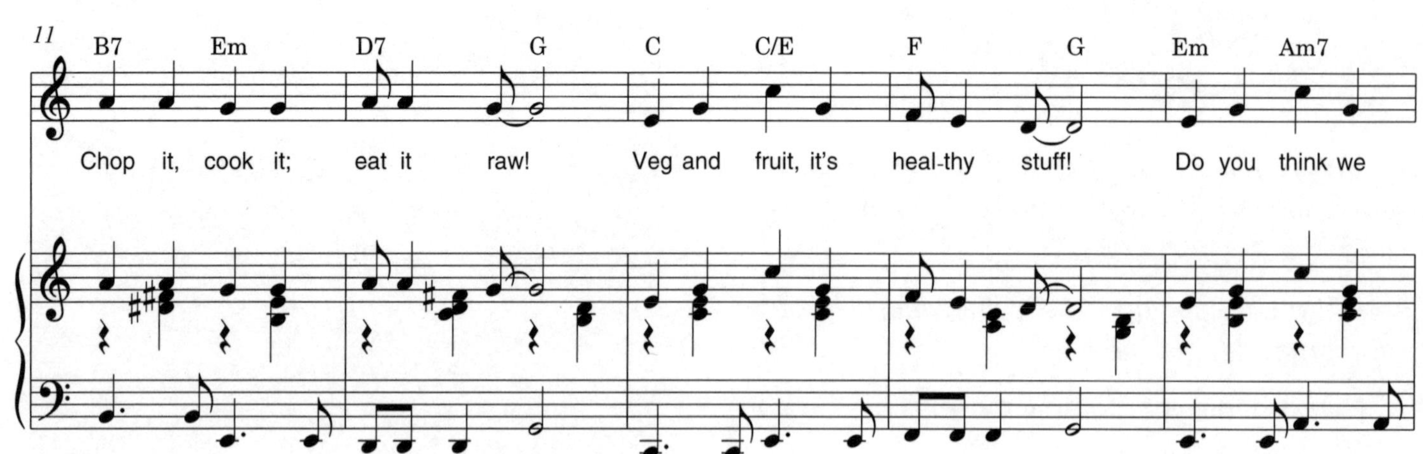
11
B7 Em D7 G C C/E F G Em Am7
Chop it, cook it; eat it raw! Veg and fruit, it's heal-thy stuff! Do you think we

Singing Sherlock wants to know:

- Can you make the word "yummy" sound really mouth-watering so that the audience feel hungry?
- Are you using your question mark face when you sing the words "Do we really eat enough?"
- Can you make up some funky moves to perform whilst you sing?

*   *Start by teaching the chant, making sure the children are confident with the words.*
*   *Children can hold up fingers for the numbers.*
*   *Make sure the children remember that in the last bar of the song the melody goes up. Similarly be careful the children do not muddle this final bar with "eat enough?" in bar 8.*
*   *Children could contribute their own vegetable and fruit ideas for new chant verses.*

Sitting on the Bus

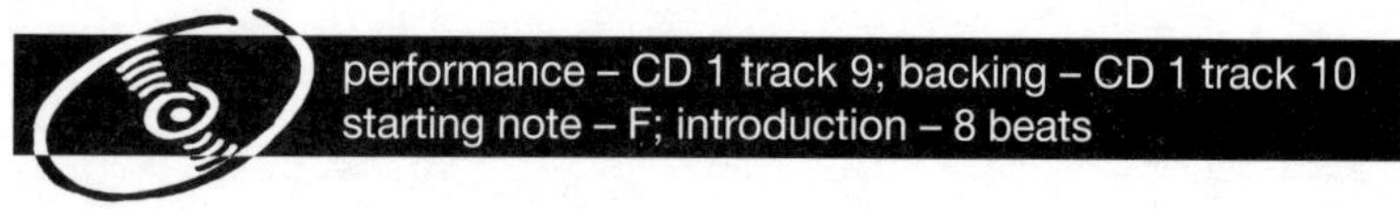

Jon Laird

Count in:

1 2 3 4

Verse 1 – *sing three times, following the instructions given in the case notes*

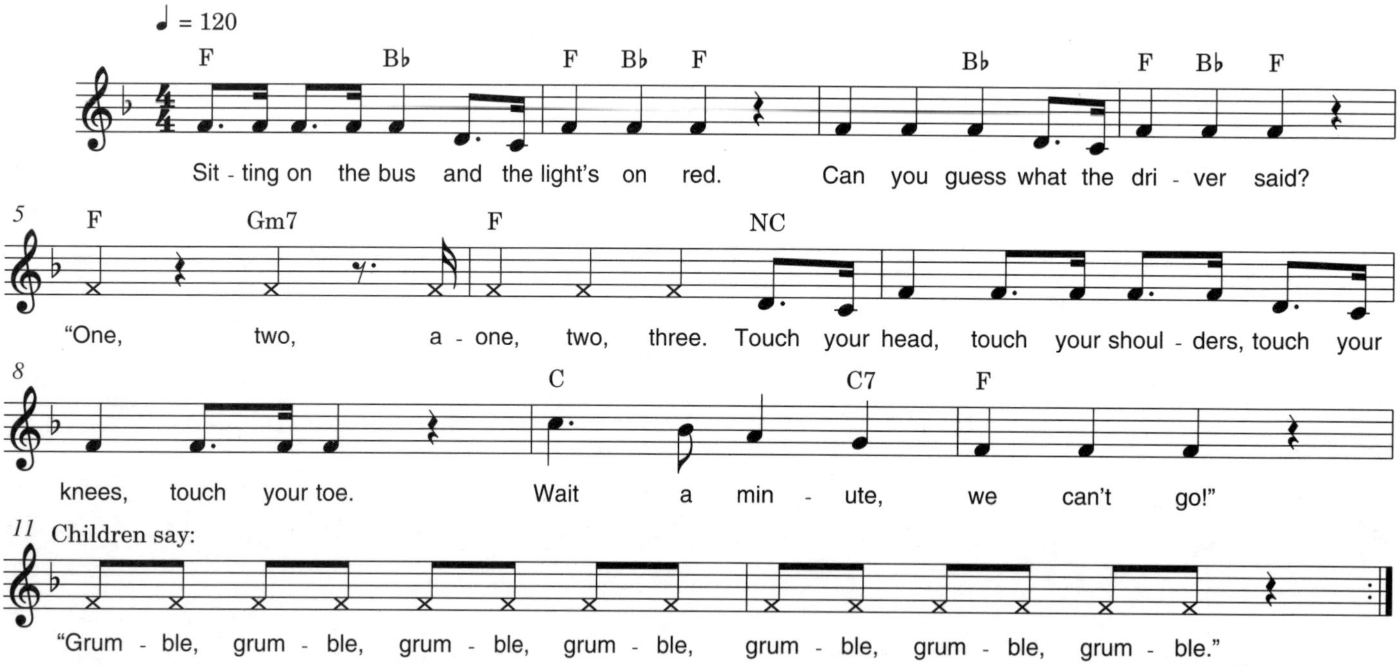

♩ = 120

F Bb F Bb F Bb F Bb F

Sit - ting on the bus and the light's on red. Can you guess what the dri - ver said?

5 F Gm7 F NC

"One, two, a - one, two, three. Touch your head, touch your shoul - ders, touch your

8 C C7 F

knees, touch your toe. Wait a min - ute, we can't go!"

11 Children say:

"Grum - ble, grum - ble, grum - ble, grum - ble, grum - ble, grum - ble, grum - ble."

Verse 2

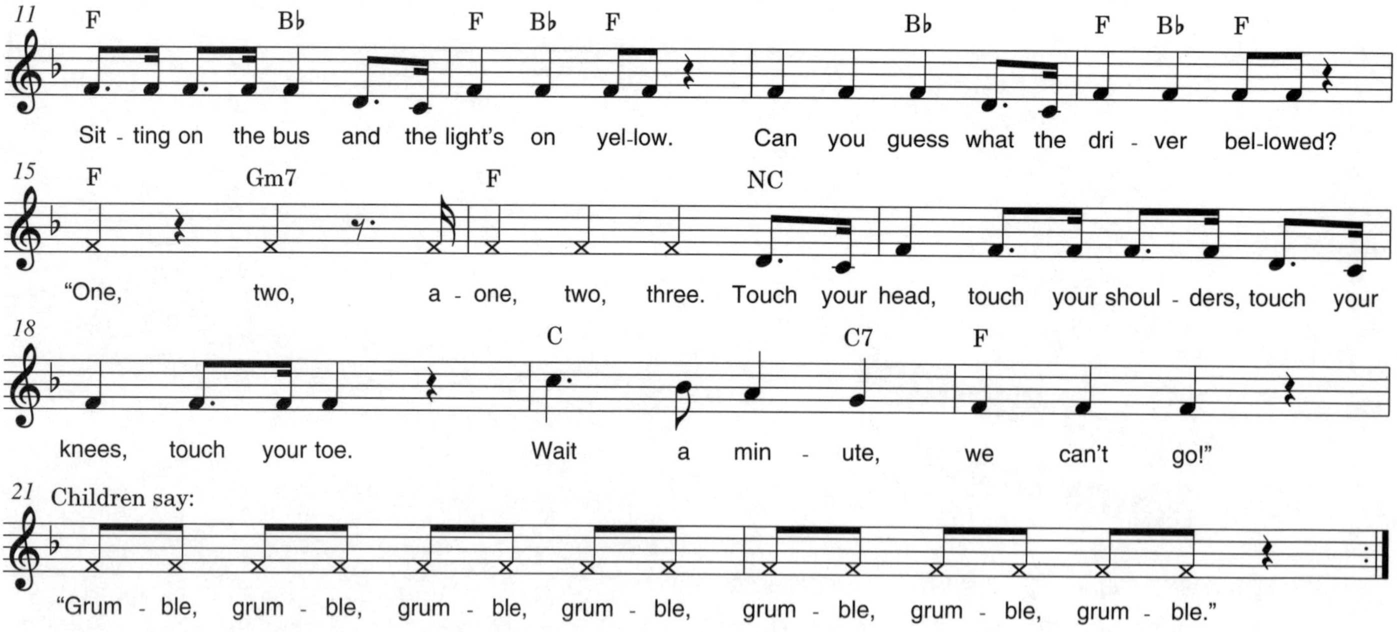

11 F Bb F Bb F Bb F Bb F

Sit - ting on the bus and the light's on yel-low. Can you guess what the dri - ver bel-lowed?

15 F Gm7 F NC

"One, two, a - one, two, three. Touch your head, touch your shoul - ders, touch your

18 C C7 F

knees, touch your toe. Wait a min - ute, we can't go!"

21 Children say:

"Grum - ble, grum - ble, grum - ble, grum - ble, grum - ble, grum - ble, grum - ble."

Singing Sherlock BOOK 3

Val Whitlock & Shirley Court

Sitting on the Bus

Verse 1 (sing three times)
Sitting on the bus and the light's on red.
Can you guess what the driver said?
"One, two, a-one, two, three.
Touch your head, touch your shoulders,
Touch your knees, touch your toe.
Wait a minute, we can't go!"

(spoken)
"Grumble, grumble, grumble, grumble, grumble, grumble, grumble."

Verse 2 ✶
Sitting on the bus and the light's on yellow.
Can you guess what the driver bellowed?
"One, two, a-one, two, three.
Touch your head, touch your shoulders,
Touch your knees, touch your toe.
Wait a minute, we can't go!"

(spoken)
"Grumble, grumble, grumble, grumble, grumble, grumble, grumble."

Verse 3 ✶
Sitting on the bus and the light's on green.
Can you guess the driver screamed?
"One, two, a-one, two, three.
Touch your head, touch your shoulders,
Touch your knees, touch your toe.
Are you ready? Off we go!"

(spoken)
Vroom!

Jon Laird

✶*See the instructions in* Sherlock's Case Notes *on page 23 on how to use your 'thinking' voice in verses 2 and 3*

Boosey & Hawkes Music Publishers Ltd
www.boosey.com

Verse 3

Children all say "**vroom**" like a bus starting up!

- Are you touching the correct parts of the body at the right time?
- Are you concentrating and remembering to use your thinking voice?
- Are you still singing the words "touch your" when you leave out the words "head", "shoulders", "knees" and "toes"?
- Can you feel your tummy muscles working as you make the "vroom" sound of the bus starting off?

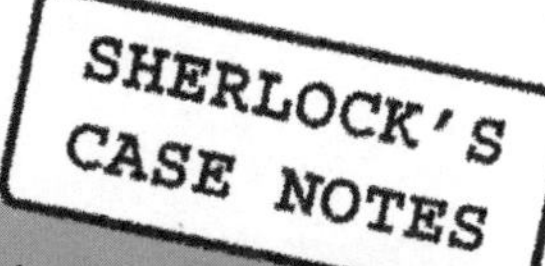

- *This works in a similar way to the song* Heads, Shoulders, Knees and Toes *and develops the 'thinking voice' as well as coordinating body movements whilst singing.*
- *Perform the song as follows:*

  – sing verse 1 three times;
  1st time as written
  2nd time leave out "head"
  3rd time leave out "head" and "shoulder"
  – sing the yellow light verse once only;
  leave out "head", "shoulders" and "knees"
  – sing the green light verse once only;
  leave out "head", "shoulders", "knees" and "toes".

- *Each time the children omit a word they should use their 'thinking voice' and sing the word 'in their head' whilst still performing the relevant action.*
- *Explain to the children that they sing the 1st verse three times because it always seems that cars have to wait a long time when the light is on red!*
- *On the "grumbles" the children need to fold their arms and look very cross!*

Everybody Silly Body Song

Rebecca Lawrence

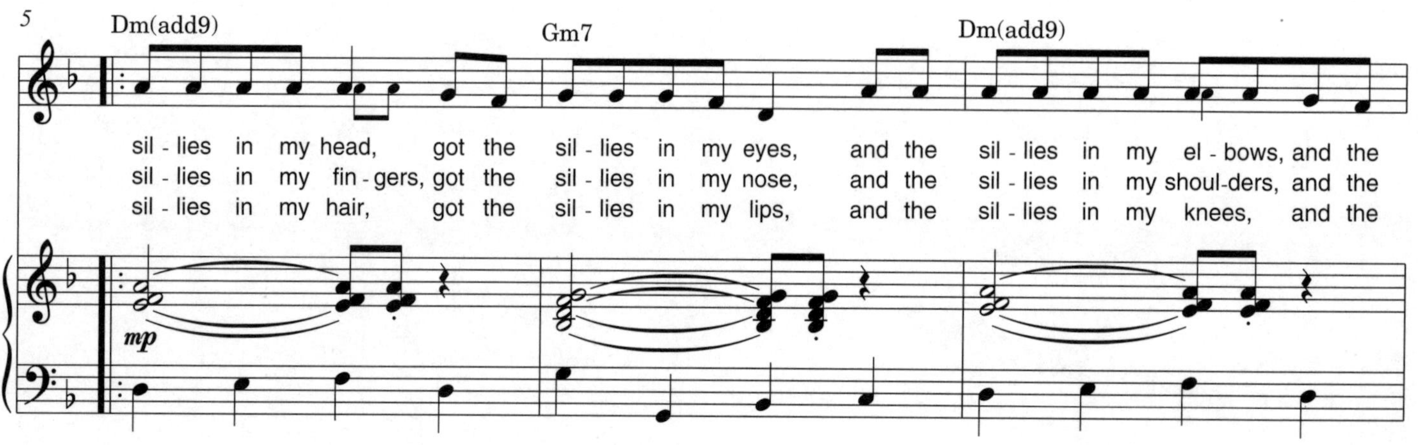

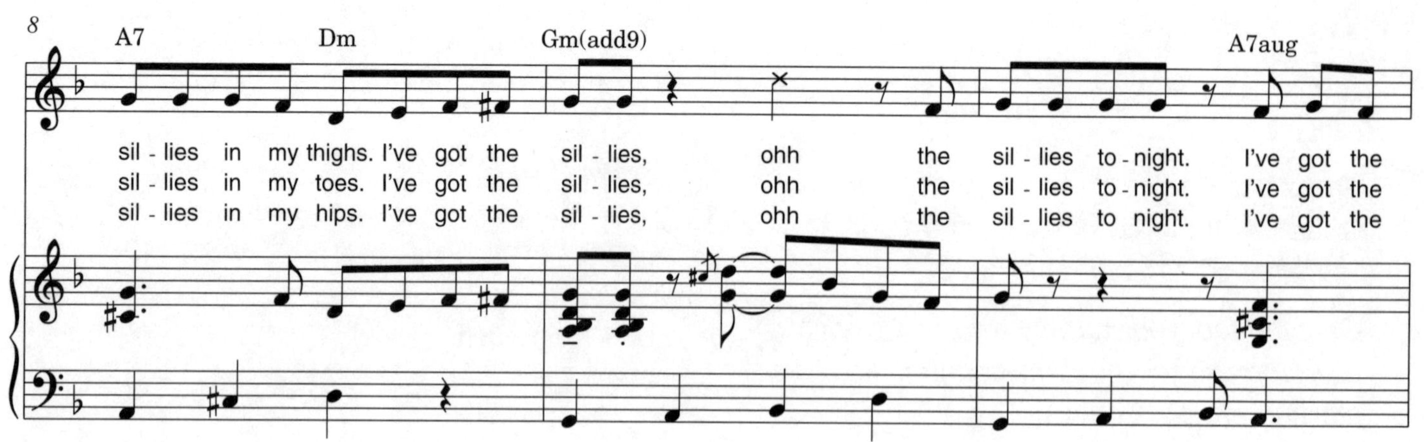

11 Dm

sil - lies, ohh the sil - lies to - night. __

sil - lies, ohh the sil - lies to - night. __

1.2 A7 *mf*

Whoah, ______

14 Gm Dm A NC *mp*

__ got the sil - lies to - night! __ I've got the

3 A7 *mf*

13b

Whoah, ______ Gm NC got the sil - lies to - night! __ Dm

mp

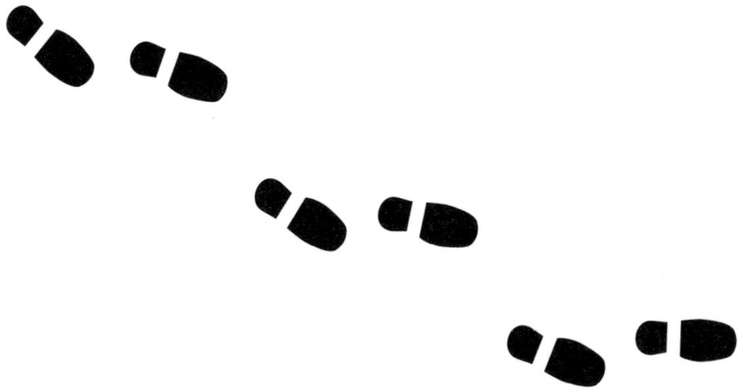

- Are you able to keep singing whilst you point to the different parts of your body?
- Are you all making the "ohh" sound at exactly the same time?
- Are you able to hold on to the last note "night" for its full length?

SHERLOCK'S CASE NOTES

- *Teach the song over a period of time so that the children do not get mixed up with the different parts of the body in each verse.*
- *It may help to have flashcards with pictures or the names of the different body parts.*
- *Ask the children to draw a rainbow shape or arc in the sky as they sing the phrase "Whoah" (bar 13). This movement will help them feel the shape of the phrase, and will free up their voices to sing the full-length of the note.*
- *At bar 8 the children will need to listen very carefully in order to sing the small steps (semitones) on the words "I've got the sillies".*
- *Encourage the children to jiggle their bodies in time with the music*
- *After verse 3 you can insert an optional instrumental verse, where the children could add other movements such as a hand-jive before singing verse 4. NB This instrumental verse is included on both the vocal and instrumental tracks on the CD.*

Kapulu Kane (Puili Game)

performance – CD 1 track 13; backing – CD 1 track 14
starting note – C; introduction – 8 beats

Hawaiian Traditional

- Can you keep the pulse in time with your singing?
- Are your words really clear?
- Are you being sensible when you clap your partner's hands?
- Are you sitting tall like a giraffe?

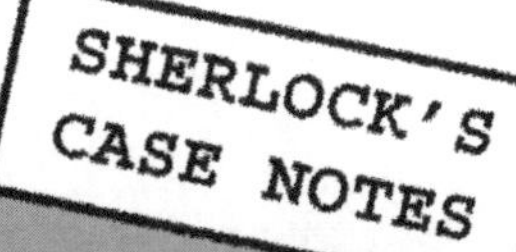

- *Puili are ancient percussion instruments used by Hawaiian dancers as part of their choreography, which also add a rhythmic accompaniment. They are bamboo sticks with a split cut at one end and make a light, rhythmic sound when tapped.*
- *"Kapulu" means messy, "kane" means man, "kuka" means coat and "nalu" means lost; so we think this might mean the messy man has lost his coat!*
- *Teach the song in stages. Firstly ask the children to repeat the words "kapulu", then "kapulu pulu", then "kane" before repeating the whole phrase "Kapulu pulu kane". Do the same thing with the phrase "kukanalua", splitting the syllables up then adding them together until the children are confident to repeat the whole phrase.*
- *Next add the melody to the words.*
- *Sit in a circle and ask the children to patsch the pulse on their knees whilst singing the song.*
- *Next, ask the children to face a partner, patsch their own knees and then clap their partner's hands to the pulse.*
- *When the children can manage these movements you could add more actions, eg slap the floor, patsch on their knees and clap their partner's hands twice.*
- *Small groups of children could use claves as substitute puili and tap the floor, or tap their partner's sticks.*

First Couple Up

performance – CD 1 track 15; backing – CD 1 track 16
starting note – G; introduction – 8 beats

American Traditional

Count in: 1 2 3 4

♩ = 90
B♭ F E♭ A7
(A) The first cou - ple up to the cou - ple on the right, (B) take a look at the

4
B♭ F E♭
North - ern lights. (C) In - to the i - gloo through the door,

7
A7 B♭ F
(D) turn a - round and clap all four. (E) Out of the i - gloo and

10
E♭ A7 B♭
in - to the ring, (F) and give your hon - ey a great big swing!

- *Are you remembering to sing whilst you dance?*
- *Can you walk in time to the music as you sing "The first couple up to the couple on the right"?*
- *Are you dancing well together as you "give your honey a great big swing?"*
- *Can you turn around quickly when you sing the words "turn around" so that you are ready to clap as you sing "clap all four"?*

SHERLOCK'S CASE NOTES

- *This is an American traditional square dance to the English tune 'Little Brown Jug'.*
- *Teach the song first before attempting the square dance.*
- *It is important to build up the movements to the dance in stages rather than trying to teach them all in one go. This may take several sessions.*
- *When the children can sing the song confidently ask them to form squares, eight children in each, with a couple on each side facing inward.*

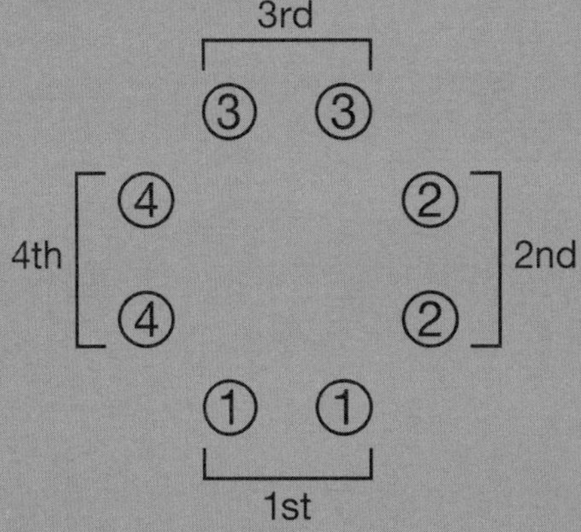

- *Next, sing the song, adding in only the turn and clap movements at "turn around and clap all four".*
- *Once the children have mastered this, you can teach the rest of the dance as follows:*
- *A – The first couple walks to face couple 2.*
- *B – With hands on hips, couples 1 and 2 point up at the lights in the sky (encourage the children to point upwards rather than tipping their heads back which will prevent them from singing).*
- *C – Couple 1 goes under an arch made by couple 2's arms.*
- *D – Couples 1 and 2 clap twice as they sing "clap all four".*
- *E – Couple 1 re-enters the square, through the arch.*
- *F – Couple 1 holds hands and swings around once and returns to their original place.*
- *The dance is then repeated with couple 2 walking to face couple 3 etc.*

Section 2 – Tune In!

Songs

Clues on how to find the singing voice and sing in tune

Everyone can do it!

Let's explode the myth about singing in tune – given the right opportunity *everyone* can do it (unless there is damage to the vocal folds or eardrum). It is a perfectly normal activity and we should be encouraging children to sing as naturally as they speak. If children's pre-school experience of singing, *eg* 'pat-a-cake' games, bouncing and singing on somebody's lap, or playground circle games in a nursery school, is very limited, they may not yet be able to pitch accurately. These kind of activities are becoming more rare and sadly are often replaced by TV progammes, CDs and DVDs. Children may still use a speaking voice or sing on a monotone rather than pitching the intervals between the notes.

Voice stretch

Children need to be given opportunities to 'find' their singing voice. Spoken rhymes and chants that can be performed with larger-than-life expression will develop the children's vocal flexibility as well as their skills in communicating words. Vocal games and warm-ups (*see pages 6–9*) where children have the chance to 'play' with their voices will exercise and stretch the vocal mechanism. Children will be able to swoop and slide their voices across a very wide pitch range (*see for example 'Wesley Bear's Day at the Office', page 9*). However the range of notes *in a song* that they can pitch accurately may well be quite narrow (although as in all subject areas at school there will always be the exceptional child).

Pitch pointers

When learning to sing young children will use a mixture of experimentation, imitation and listening in order to match their pitch to another voice. The vocal folds of young children are very tiny and when learning to sing they only have a small number of notes. Initially this may be a kind of 'prox-pitch' where they follow the contour of a tune before pitching accurately. Using very simple songs that contain two or three notes and in particular the interval of a minor 3rd (sometimes called the 'cuckoo' notes or 'playground chant') allows children to match their voices most successfully. (NB The minor 3rd interval is universally accepted as the easiest for children to sing in the first stages of their vocal development.) Once a child has begun to pitch some of these notes, there begins the process of gaining the finer control needed to produce more extended melodies.

Not too high, not too low

Be careful with the vocal range of songs; they should be neither too high nor too low, nor contain too many wide interval leaps. Generally children go through the following stages when learning to control their voices:

- playing with their voices through babbling and swooping etc
- singing on one or two pitches, *ie* chanting
- singing in a small range of notes, usually at a fairly low pitch often around D above middle C
- singing in a wider range of notes, *ie* five notes from middle C or D up to G or A above
- singing an extened range of pitches across an octave

Go solo

Children also need to hear their *own* singing voice; singing only with a larger group of children who are not yet all pitching in tune is very confusing to the child's ear. If this situation prevails then children can end up going through school never finding their singing voice and never being able to pitch accurately. Some children, in their efforts to hear their own voice will try to compete with the sound and either shout or sing much higher. It is vital for small children to sing songs that give opportunities for an individual response, *eg Calico* (*page 40*), *The Dolphin Song* (*page 93*) and *The Noisy House* (*page 57*). All these songs contain the interval of a minor 3rd (*see pitch pointers on the previous page*). Singing in small groups, pairs and trios is also valuable, particularly when the children are initially shy about singing alone.

If you don't use it you lose it

Like any physical or muscular activity singing needs to be done frequently. In addition to scheduled singing sessions, *eg* assembly, class singing etc, sing the register or improvise vocal conversations using 'cuckoo notes', sing as you line up for dinner and sing on the carpet at storytime. All these devices will help children learn to control their voices.

Sing unaccompanied

Children will respond far better, pitch more accurately and sing with a clearer vocal tone by copying another voice rather than singing to a musical instrument or CD. It is far harder to pitch to an instrument – something even some adults can find difficult. They need to learn to compare and match their voice to that of the leader. Even with an accompanied song it is always advantageous to teach as much as possible unaccompanied.

Ear, ear!

There is a link between the voice and the ear; good listening encourages good singing and conversely good singing encourages good listening. Put strong singers between children with weaker ears or those who have not yet found their singing voices.

Did You Feed My Cow?

performance – CD 1 track 17; backing – CD 1 track 18
starting note – C; introduction – 4 beats

Lyrics Traditional
Music by Ella Jenkins

Count in: 1 2 3

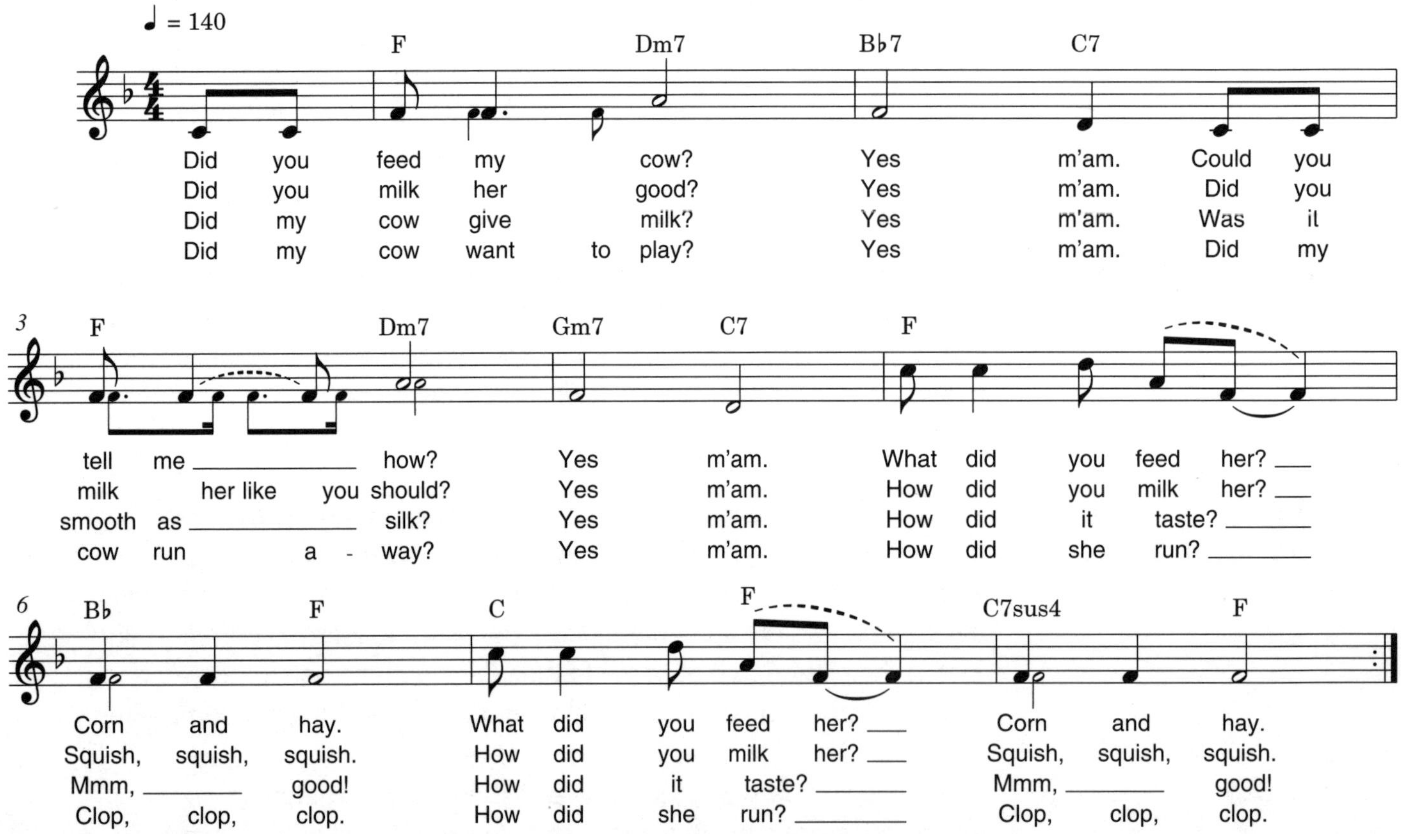

♩ = 140

F Dm7 B♭7 C7

Did you feed my cow? Yes m'am. Could you
Did you milk her good? Yes m'am. Did you
Did my cow give milk? Yes m'am. Was it
Did my cow want to play? Yes m'am. Did my

3 F Dm7 Gm7 C7 F

tell me ___ how? Yes m'am. What did you feed her? ___
milk her like you should? Yes m'am. How did you milk her? ___
smooth as ___ silk? Yes m'am. How did it taste? ___
cow run a - way? Yes m'am. How did she run? ___

6 B♭ F C F C7sus4 F

Corn and hay. What did you feed her? ___ Corn and hay.
Squish, squish, squish. How did you milk her? ___ Squish, squish, squish.
Mmm, ___ good! How did it taste? ___ Mmm, ___ good!
Clop, clop, clop. How did she run? ___ Clop, clop, clop.

- *Can you make up actions for each of the verses "Squish, squish, squish", "Mmm, good!" and "Clop, clop, clop"?*
- *Are you making this song a conversation between two characters: the farmer asking about her cow, and the herdsman who looks after the cow?*
- *As you sing "Mmm" can you feel a buzz on your lips?*
- *Are you making sure you sound the letter 'k' at the end of the words "milk" and "silk"?*

- *This is a 'call and response' song, which means the leader sings a phrase, and the singers respond with another.*
- *Begin with asking the children to join in and sing "Yes m'am". These two notes form the 'cuckoo' chant* (see Pitch Pointers on page 32), *which is universally sung by young children in the early stages of vocal development. This particular interval will help children tune in both their ears and voices.*
- *Next teach the children the leader's part.*
- *Divide the children into two groups so that half are singing the 'call' and the other half the 'response'.*
- *Once the children are really confident ask small groups or soloists to sing the 'response' phrase.*

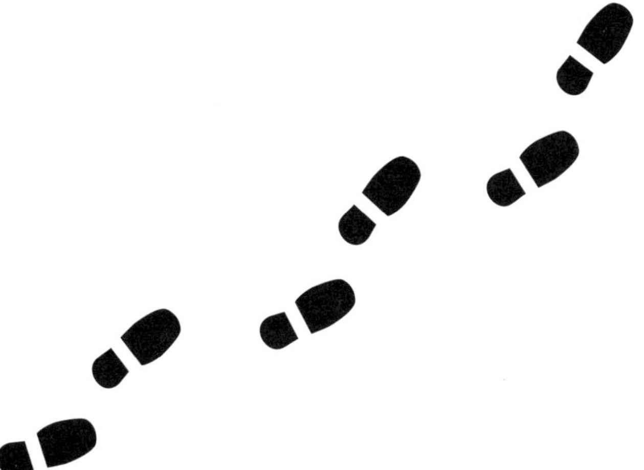

The Bird Tree

Jon Laird

♩ = 116 Count in: 1 2 3 4

D A7 | D A7 D | A7sus4

I saw a lit - tle par - rot
I saw a lit - tle hum-ming-bird
I saw a lit - tle duck
I saw a lit - tle owl
I saw a lit - tle e - mu

4 D A7sus4 | D A7 | D A7 D

danc - ing by a tree. What did he sound like? Talk with me!
fly - ing round a tree. What did he sound like? Hum with me!
flap - ping up a tree. What did he sound like? Quack with me!
sit - ting in a tree. What did he sound like? Sing with me!
peck - ing at a tree. What did he sound like? Peck with me!

7 D A7sus4 | D A7sus4 | D A7 | D A7 D

(*spoken*) Pret - ty pol - ly! Pret - ty pol - ly! Pret - ty pol - ly! Tee-hee-hee-hee-hee!
(*hummed*) Hm - mm - mm - mm. Hm - mm - mm - mm. Hm - mm - mm - mm. Hm-mm-mm-mm-mm.
(*quacked*) Wah wah wah wah. Wah wah wah wah. Wah wah wah wah. Wahwah wah wah wah.
(*sung*) Too - whit too - whit. Too - whit too - whit. Too - whit too - whit. Woo-oo - oo - oo - oo.

(*The emu does not make any sound: the children should make their fingers into an emu's nose and peck the tune using their thinking voices*)

- Do you know which different voice you are using when you sing the animal sounds?
- Are you listening carefully so you can match your voice to the leaders?
- Are you using your questioning face when you ask "What did he sound like?"

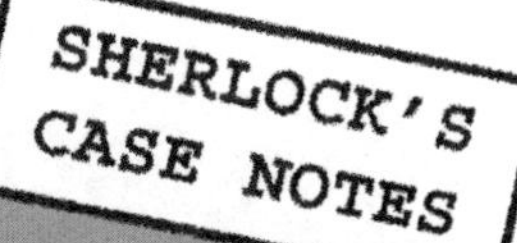

- *The first two phrases of this song use the first five notes of a (major) scale rising stepwise – 1, 2, 3, 4, 5.*
- *To develop the children's listening skills explain that the notes are 'stepping notes' (notes that are next door to one another) and ask them to hold up the relevant number of fingers as they hear the tune rise a step at a time.*
- *This song also uses the two-note 'cuckoo' interval (*bars 5, 7, 8 and 9*), which will help children tune in their ears and voices.*
- *It also creates opportunities for the children to explore and identify their different voices, for example:*

  – speaking voice (parrot)
  – humming voice (humming bird)
  – singing voice (owl)
  – twangy voice (duck)
  – thinking voice (emu)

- *When the children sing the emu part, ask them to make their fingers into an emu's nose and 'peck' the tune, whilst 'singing' the words in their head.*
- *Invite smaller groups, pairs and soloists to perform the animal voice responses.*

Five Little Leaves

performance – CD 1 track 21; backing – CD 1 track 22
starting note – A; introduction – 14 beats

Lyrics anon
Music by Ashley Thompson

Gently ♩ = 100
Count in: 1 2 3 4
G D/F# A D G/D D Em7/D D D/F# G
Five lit - tle leaves on the
Four lit - tle leaves…
Three lit - tle leaves…
Two lit - tle leaves…
One lit - tle leaf…

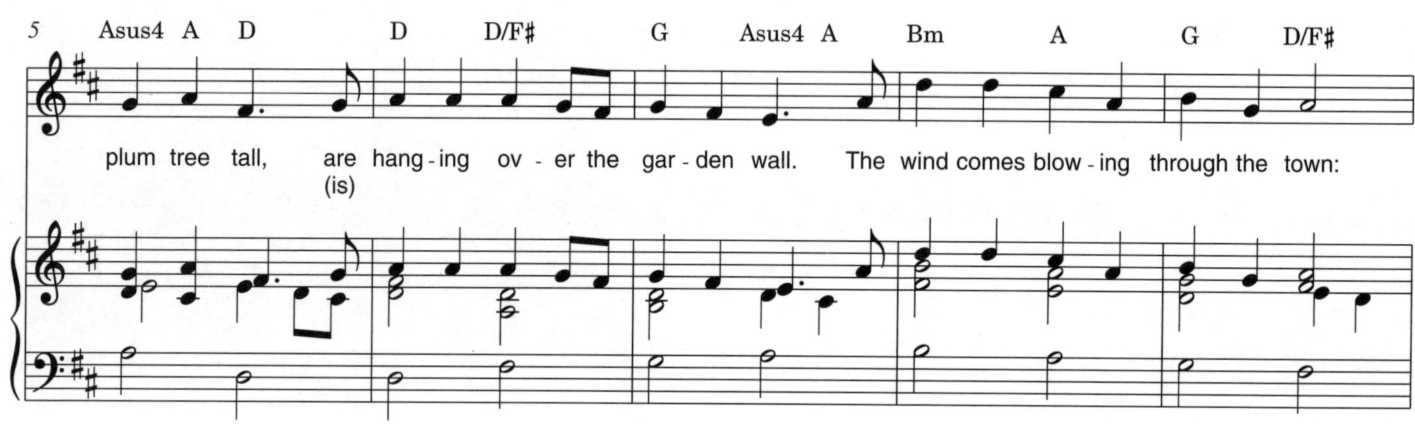
5
Asus4 A D D D/F# G Asus4 A Bm A G D/F#
plum tree tall, are hang - ing ov - er the gar - den wall. The wind comes blow - ing through the town:
(is)

10
G Asus4 A G D/F# A
1–4
D G/D D Em7/D
Oo oo oo Oooo One lit - tle leaf comes flut - ter - ing down.

13e
5
Slowly
down.
No lit - tle leaves on the plum tree tall.
D G/D D Em7/D D D/F♯ G Asus4 A D

Singing Sherlock wants to know:

- Are you making beautiful "Oo" shapes with your mouth?
- Are you singing each line of the song very smoothly?
- Do you remember how many leaves you have left when one is blown off the tree in each of the verses?
- Can you sing the last line of the song, when there are no leaves left, very quietly?
- Can you make some wind sounds in the piano introduction to the song?

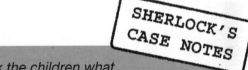

SHERLOCK'S CASE NOTES

- *Ask the children what happens to the leaves on trees when the wind blows in autumn.*
- *Begin by teaching them to sing the section where the wind blows* (bar 10). *Ask the children to make an "Oo" sound with lips together. Start with a gentle breeze. Make sure they feel the rest at the beginning of the bar – to indicate this rest, clap or make a movement before singing "Oo".*
- *For a different effect a smaller group of singers could sing the wind "Oos" – or indeed vary the number of singers in each verse if the wind gets stronger.*
- *In order to reach the higher note on the word "wind"* (bar 8) *ask the children to make their necks long like a giraffe.*
- *Make sure the children do not get the notes on "plum tree tall"* (bar 5) *muddled with "garden wall"* (bar 7).
- *Ask five children to represent each of the leaves to be blown off the tree at the appropriate moment.*

Calico is a Charming Cat

Sue Nicholls

Count in: 1 2

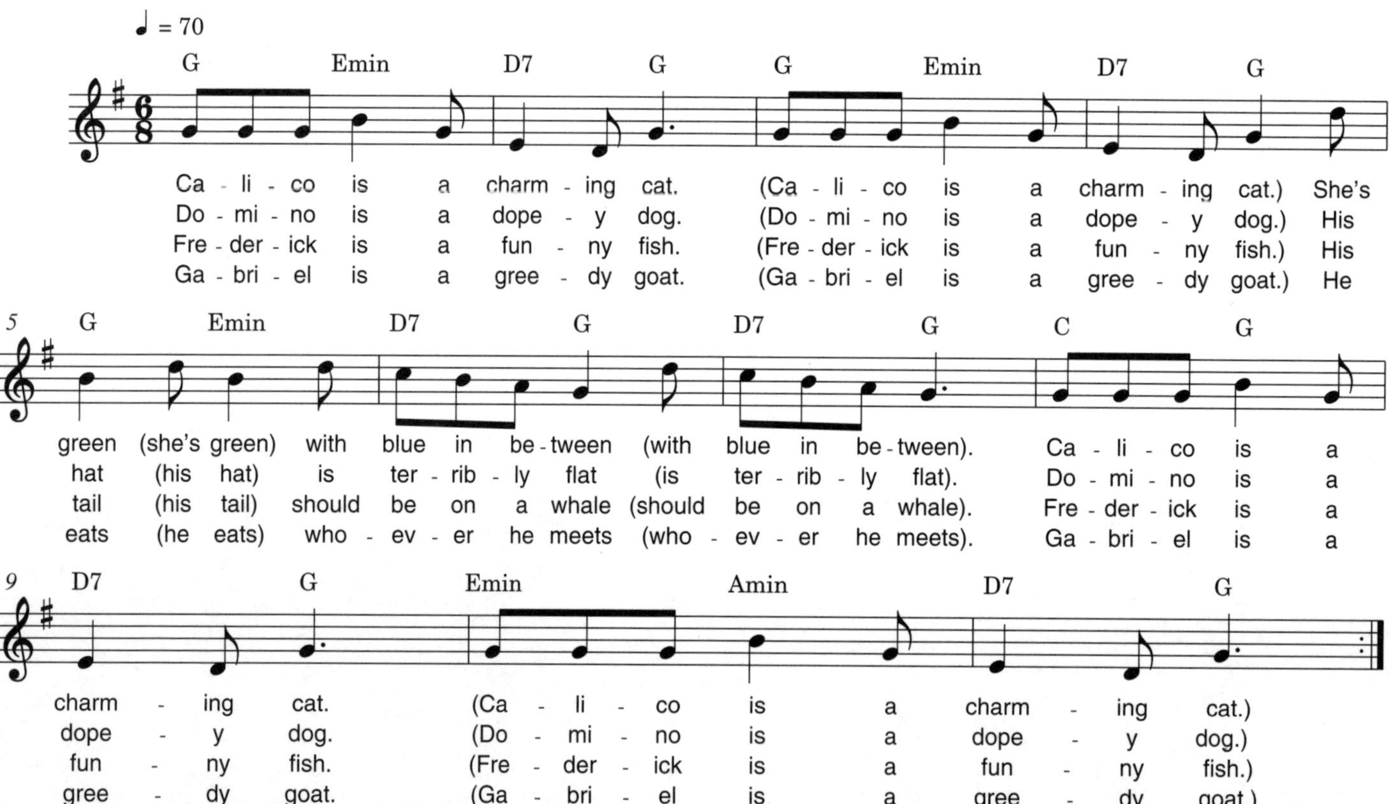

- Are you making a good clear 'c' on the word "Calico"?
- Are you making a lovely 'oo' sound on the word "blue"?
- Can you perform some actions for each verse?
- Can you make up some new verses about other animals?

SHERLOCK'S CASE NOTES

- *This is a 'call and response' song. Teach it by singing each line then asking the children to echo.*
- *Divide the class into two halves and let each group have a turn at both the call and the echo.*
- *When the children are really familiar with the song ask smaller groups, trios, duets and soloists to sing the call.*
- *Ask the children to imagine the characters of each of the animals. Can they adopt a posture that represents a charming cat, a dopey dog, a funny fish and a greedy goat as they sing?*

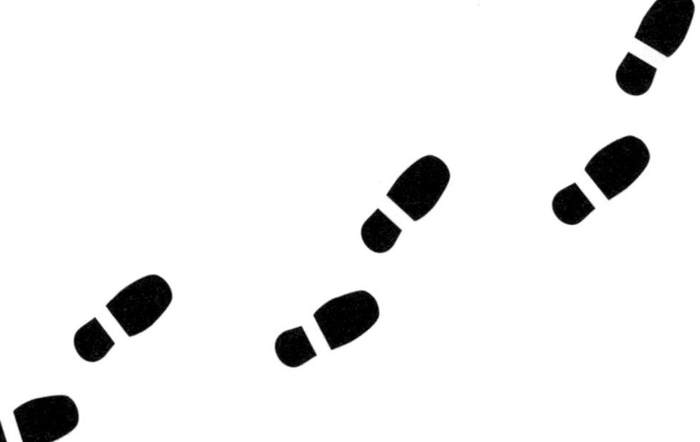

The Engine Driver

performance – CD 1 track 25; backing – CD 1 track 26
starting note – G; introduction – 16 beats

Lyrics by Clive Sansom
Music by Ashley Thompson

Lively ♩. = 100
2nd time no repeat
D G/D D G/D
Jick - et - ty - can, jick - et - ty - can, Jick - et - ty - can, jick - et - ty - can,
5
D G/D D G/D D
The train goes run-ning a - long the line, jick - et - ty - can,
10
A/D D G/D D A/D
jick - et - ty - can. I wish it were mine, I wish it were mine, jick - et - ty - can, jick - et - ty - can. The
15
D C/D B♭/C C C/E
en - gine driv - er stands in front, he makes it run, he makes it shunt;

19
F
Eb/F
F
Eb/F
out of the town, out of the town, ov - er the hill, ov - er the down.
23
D
C/D
D
Asus4/D
A/D
Un - der the bridg - es, a - cross the lea, ov - er the ridge and down to the sea.
27
D
C/D
Bb/C
C/Bb
Jick - et - ty - can, jick - et - ty - can, jick - et - ty - jick - et - ty - jick - et - ty - can,
31
Asus4
A
1
repeat from beginning
2
D
G/D
D
jick - et - ty - can, jick - et - ty - can. Jick - et - ty - can - can.

Singing Sherlock wants to know:

- *The tune of this song goes up and down in steps like the train going up and down the hills and valleys. Can you show the shape of the tune with your hands?*
- *Are you using your tongue and lips to make sure all your words are clear?*
- *Are you all performing your train connecting-rod action together and perfectly in time?*
- *Are you using your whispering voice when you chant the words of the introduction "Jickettycan"?*

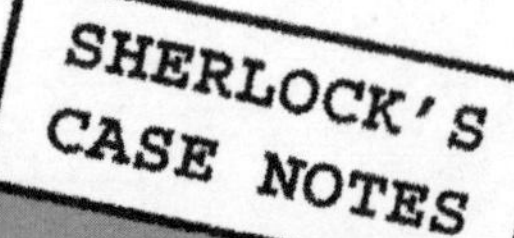

- *Although the song does not specifically refer to a steam train you could find pictures of old trains to enthuse the children about the world of steam.*
- *You will need to explain the word "lea", which means valley.*
- *Speak the words in rhythm before teaching the tune. Ask the children to patsch the pulse at the same time to keep the words steady, rather than letting them rush away.*
- *To ensure the children can whisper "Jickettycan" really clearly ask them to articulate just the consonants of the words, eg j, k, t, c, n etc.*
- *The unexpected F♮ on the words "makes it run"* (bar 17) *will need some practice, as indeed will the return to the F♯ on "over the ridge"* (bar 25).
- *To set the scene one child could blow a train whistle either before the song starts, or during the rest bars after the "Jickettycan" introduction.*
- *The children could perform pumping arm actions to represent the connection rods of the train's wheels as they whisper the words "Jickettycan".*

Animals Live in the Forest

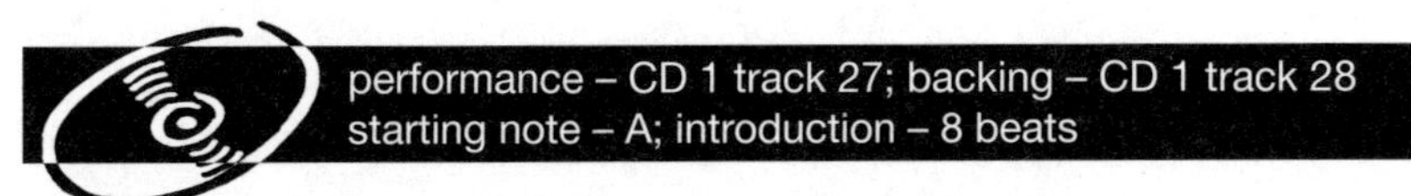

performance – CD 1 track 27; backing – CD 1 track 28
starting note – A; introduction – 8 beats

B Joan E Haines

Count in: 1 2 3 4

2. Animals live in the forest,
   Animals live in the zoo.
   I met a lion in the shopping mall!
   Here's what he taught me to do:
   "Roar!" said the lion, "Gr, gr, gr, gr!"
   "Hug!" said the brown bear, "Hug, hug, hug, hug!"
   That's what they taught me to do!

3. Animals live in the forest,
   Animals live in the zoo.
   I met a mouse in the shopping mall!
   Here's what he taught me to do:
   "Eek!" said the little mouse, "Eek, eek, eek, eek!"
   "Roar!" said the lion, "Gr, gr, gr, gr!"
   "Hug!" said the brown bear, "Hug, hug, hug, hug!"
   That's what they taught me to do!

4. Animals live in the forest,
   Animals live in the zoo.
   I met a kangaroo in the shopping mall!
   Here's what he taught me to do:
   "Jump!" said the kangaroo, "Jump, jump, jump, jump!"
   "Eek!" said the little mouse, "Eek, eek, eek, eek!"
   "Roar!" said the lion, "Gr, gr, gr, gr!"
   "Hug!" said the brown bear, "Hug, hug, hug, hug!"
   That's what they taught me to do!

5. Animals live in the forest,
   Animals live in the zoo.
   I met a dolphin in the shopping mall!
   Here's what he taught me to do:
   "Dive!" said the dolphin, "Dive, dive, dive, dive!"
   "Jump!" said the kangaroo, "Jump, jump, jump, jump!"
   "Eek!" said the little mouse, "Eek, eek, eek, eek!"
   "Roar!" said the lion, "Gr, gr, gr, gr!"
   "Hug!" said the brown bear, "Hug, hug, hug, hug!"
   That's what they taught me to do!

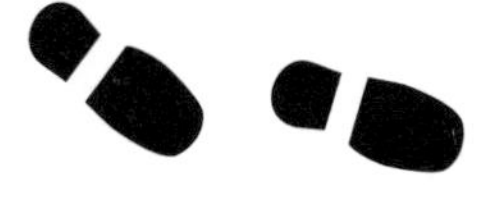

- Put your hands on your tummy as you say the words. Can you feel your tummy muscles working when you make the four bear hug sounds?
- Are your mouse "Eeks" high and squeaky?
- When the kangaroo says "Jump" can you make your voice go from low to high?
- When the dolphin says "Dive" can you make your voice go from high to low?
- Can you remember all the animal verses in the correct order?

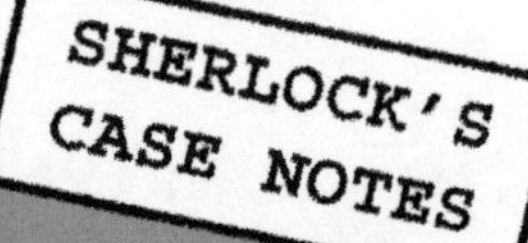

- *This is a cumulative song where the new animal and action is added first, so that each verse ends with the four bear hugs.*
- *Make sure the children sing four hugs: they have a tendency to stop after three.*
- *Divide the children into four animal groups – lion, mouse, kangaroo and dolphin. Everyone sings the song until the repeating bars* (bar 9 and 10), *which should be sung by the relevant animal group. Everyone joins in with bear hugs and the last line "That's what they taught me to do!"*
- *When the children are confident, you can invite smaller groups or soloists to sing the repeating bars with the rest of the group joining in the actions and animal sounds.*

Engineers

performance – CD 1 track 29; backing – CD 1 track 30
starting note – G; introduction – 8 beats

Lyrics by Kaye Umansky
Music by Ashley Thompson

Boogie woogie ♩ = 140
NC
F♯
G

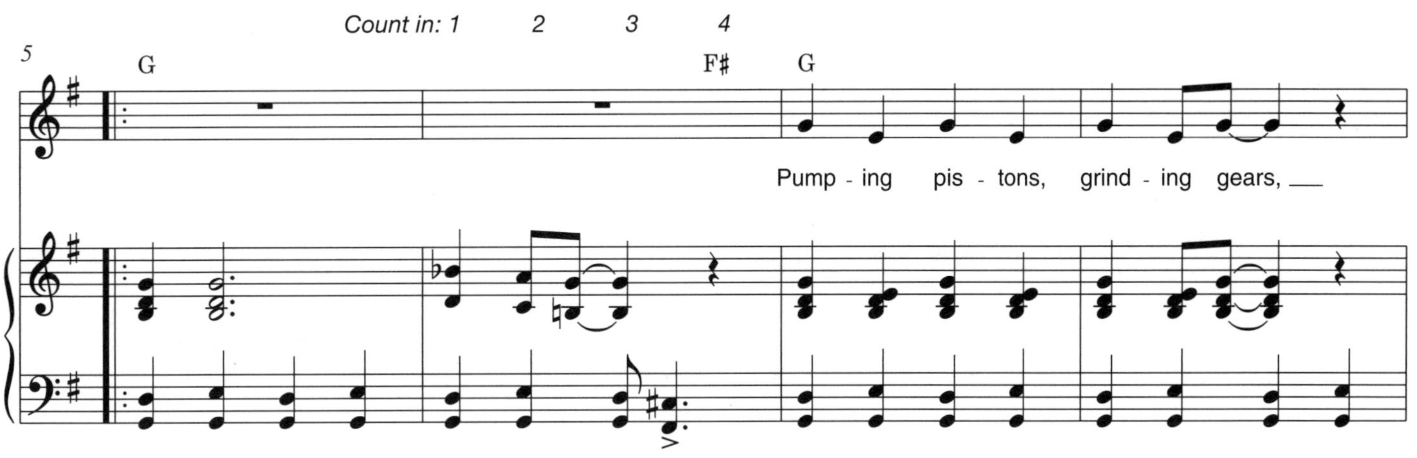
Count in: 1 2 3 4
5
G
F♯
G
Pump - ing pis - tons, grind - ing gears, ___

9
C
G
F♯
G
that is mu - sic to our ears. ___ Add a drop of

12
C
G
lub - ri - ca - tion, all ma-chines in op - er - a - tion.
15
B♭/E♭
B♭m7
Bring on the sound we love to hear, the en - gines roar - ing
18
G
Dsus4
in our ear. We wan - na say it loud and clear, it's great to be
22
D
1
G
2
NC
G
an en - gi - neer.
- neer.

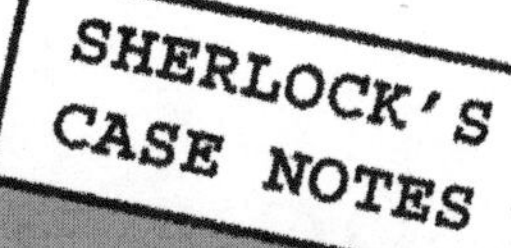

- *This song is influenced by Boogie Woogie, an early form of jazz and blues played on the piano with a repeated riff or pattern in the left hand.*
- *The opening bars of the song make use of the 'cuckoo' interval (a minor 3rd).*
- *Describe the job of an engineer, and what the words "piston" and "lubrication" mean.*
- *Help the children to feel the rests in this song by clapping or making a movement. For example clap twice after the words "grinding gears" before singing "that is music to our ears"* (bar 9). *Clap once only after the words "drop of lubrication" and before singing "all machines in operation"* (bar 13).
- *You will also need to point out the difference in the tune during these bars.*

Singing Sherlock wants to know:

- *Once you have practised clapping the rests in the song and are confident you know when they come, can you perform it without clapping?*
- *Can you make up some actions to the song that show you are a busy engineer?*
- *Are you using your lips and tongue to sound the words "pumping pistons" and "grinding gears"?*

Sherlock's Sports Day

performance – CD 1 track 31; backing – CD 1 track 32
starting note – E; introduction – 8 beats

Sue Nicholls

Lively ♩ = 90
G
Cdim7/G
G
Dsus4
G
C
[Introductory instrumental verse]
[Verse 1] Sher-lock's ve - ry
[Final verse] Sher-lock's ve - ry

Count in: 1 2
6
G
C
Dm7
G
F
Dm7
C
Dm7
G7
1
C
2
C
FINE
[Verse 1] Our
spor-ty. He trains through-out the year. He's warm-ing up be - side the track 'cos Sports Day's here!
spor-ty. He trains through-out the year. The champ is run-ning round the track so give a cheer!

13
G
Cdim7/G
G
Dsus4
G
C
Am
Dm7
G
(spoken) Please get ready for the sprint race!
(spoken) Please get ready for the hurdles race!
(spoken) Please get ready for the sack race!
(spoken) Please get ready for the obstacle race!
(spoken) Please get ready for the awards ceremony!
Run-ning on the grass track,
Leap-ing ov - er hur - dles, _
Hop-ping in the sack race, _
Run-ning, leap-ing, hop - ping, _
Stand-ing on the plat - form, _

repeat bars 13–24 x 5
Last time DS al Fine
19
Dm7 G7 C C7 F D7/F♯ G G7 C
run - ning to and fro: You're such a sport - ing le - gend, Sher-lock! Go, go, go!
leap - ing to and fro: You're such a sport - ing le - gend, Sher-lock! Go, go, go!
hop - ing to and fro: You're such a sport - ing le - gend, Sher-lock! Go, go, go!
go - ing to and fro: You're such a sport - ing le - gend, Sher-lock! Go, go, go!
do - ing as he's told: You've won each sport - ing con - test, Sher-lock! Gold, gold, gold! Our

Singing Sherlock wants to know:

- Can you show with your hand where the tune goes up and goes down?
- Are you making the muscles in your tongue and lips work hard, making all the beginnings and endings of words clear, eg "Sherlock", "track", "sack", "gold" etc?
- Are you giving Sherlock a big cheer and a round of applause at the end of the song?

SHERLOCK'S CASE NOTES

- *This song has a melody that explores both stepwise movement (notes that are next door to one another) and small interval jumps.*
- ***Performance suggestion***

  Everyone performs the actions for the introductory instrumental verse as follows:
  line 1 – alternate fists punched in the air four times
  line 2 – two star jumps
  line 3 – jogging on the spot
  line 4 – four knee bends

- *Choose a small group of children to act out the different races – running, leaping, hopping – in each verse, while the rest of the children sing.*
- *Ask all the children to cup their hands around their mouth when they use their 'megaphone voice' to announce the races. Alternatively, choose three children to announce each race.*

Section 3 – Sing the Story

Clues on communicating and expressing a song

Focus and attention

From the outset ensure the children make eye contact with you, including even the youngest children in reception classes. You can give the children a focal point to perform to such as a soft toy, picture or clock on the wall. Make sure all the children can see the leader – you may want to place taller children behind smaller children.

Storytelling

Singing is just the same as acting, but the words are set to music. The children need to engage with the story of the song and communicate it to the audience. Ask the children to think about what kind of face to wear when singing a particular song – do they need to wear an angry, happy, shocked or a question mark face? Use a child as a 'Sherlock TV detector' to check all the faces are switched on.

Movement and actions

Actions help children to remember the words and internalise musical concepts such as pulse and rhythm. Actions also enhance the performance visually, and can help children express the words of a song more vividly. However it is important that actions are not too complicated, so that they neither hinder the quality nor visually detract from the singing.

Lips and tongue

To help children enunciate their words they need to use their lips and tongue efficiently. Use the following steps:
- speak the words very slowly
- use different voices, *eg* a posh lady, a Dalek or Bugs Bunny
- whisper the words with an exaggerated mouth

Chants like *Jimbo Jambo* (*page 7*) are also valuable for exercising these muscles.

Make Friends Around the World

Kaye Umansky

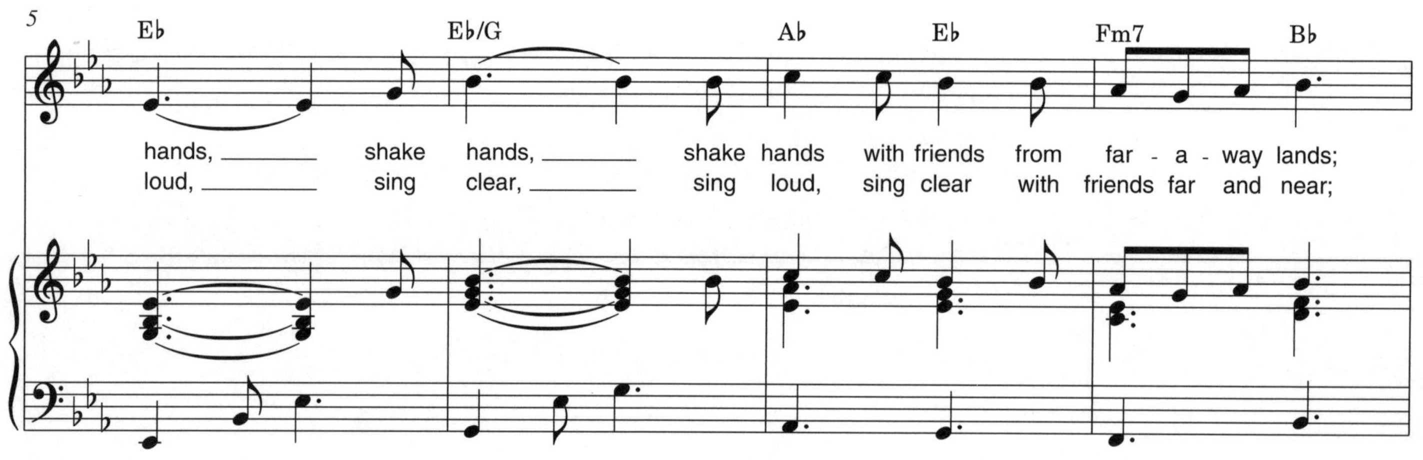

13
Eb
Eb/Bb
Bb
Bb7/D
Eb
Make friends a - round the world, it's ea - sy if you try. What -
17
Ab
Eb/Bb
Bbsus4
Bb
Eb
- ev - er the wea - ther, we live to - ge - ther be - neath the same blue sky.
21
Eb
Eb/Bb
Bb
Bb7/D
Eb
Make friends a - round the world, it's ea - sy if you try. What -
25
Ab
Eb/Bb
Bbsus4
Bb
Eb
- ev - er the wea - ther, we live to - ge - ther be - neath the same blue sky.

- Are you looking at your partner as you shake their hand?
- Are you shaking hands gently, and keeping in time with the music?
- Are you wearing a happy face when you spread your smiles across the miles?

SHERLOCK'S CASE NOTES

- *This simple but effective song has a sincere message that children of this age will instantly relate to. It would be a useful song to sing in assembly.*
- *Sit the children in a circle, holding hands. As you sing, shake your hands up and down to the pulse.*
- *Each child could also turn to a partner and shake hands as if meeting them for the first time.*
- *The children can draw a smile in the air with their hands as they sing "spread your smiles across the miles".*
- *If the children are very young you may need to explain the word "mile".*

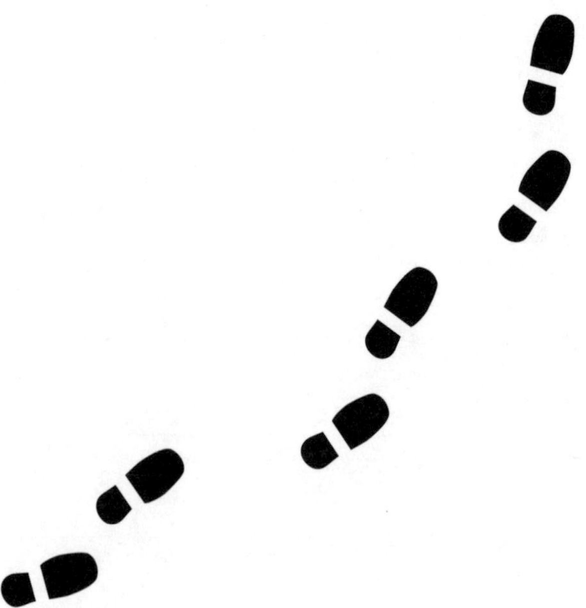

The Noisy House

CHORUS
19
D Bm G D G A7sus4 D A7 D G A7
When I lis-ten then I can see what a noi - sy house this seems to be!

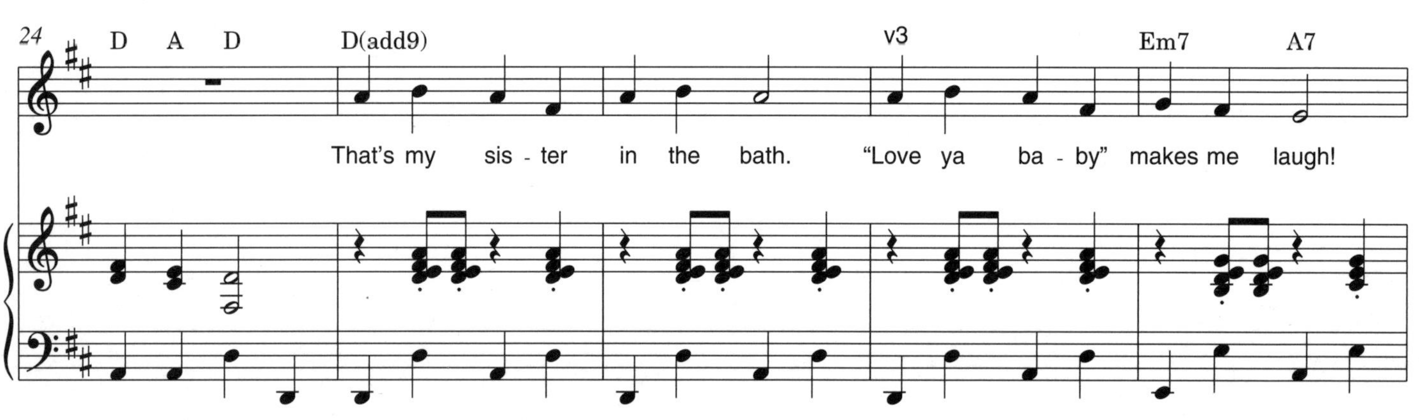
24
D A D D(add9) v3 Em7 A7
That's my sis - ter in the bath. "Love ya ba - by" makes me laugh!

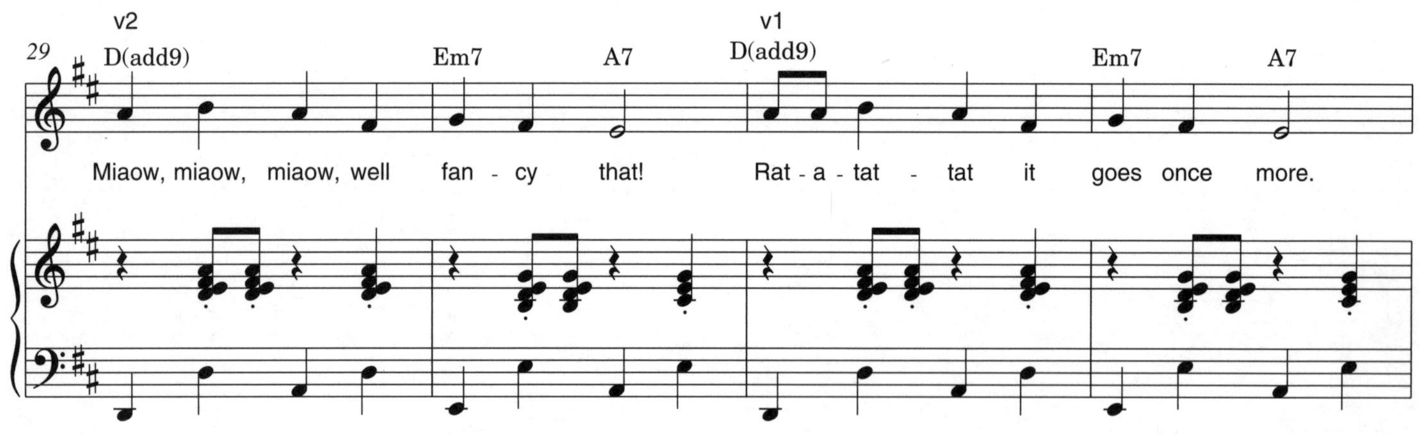
v2 v1
29
D(add9) Em7 A7 D(add9) Em7 A7
Miaow, miaow, miaow, well fan - cy that! Rat - a - tat - tat it goes once more.

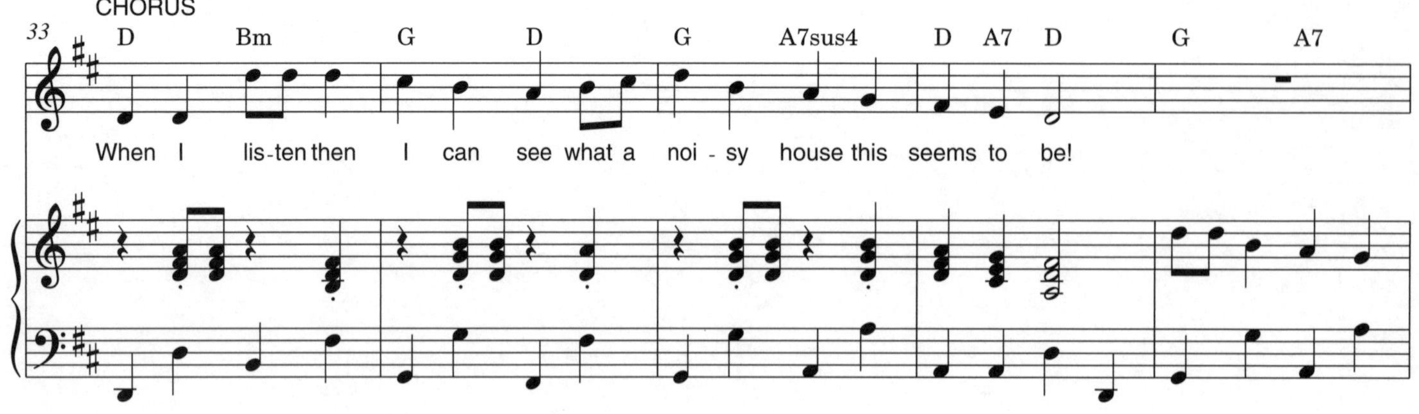
CHORUS
33
D Bm G D G A7sus4 D A7 D G A7
When I lis-ten then I can see what a noi - sy house this seems to be!

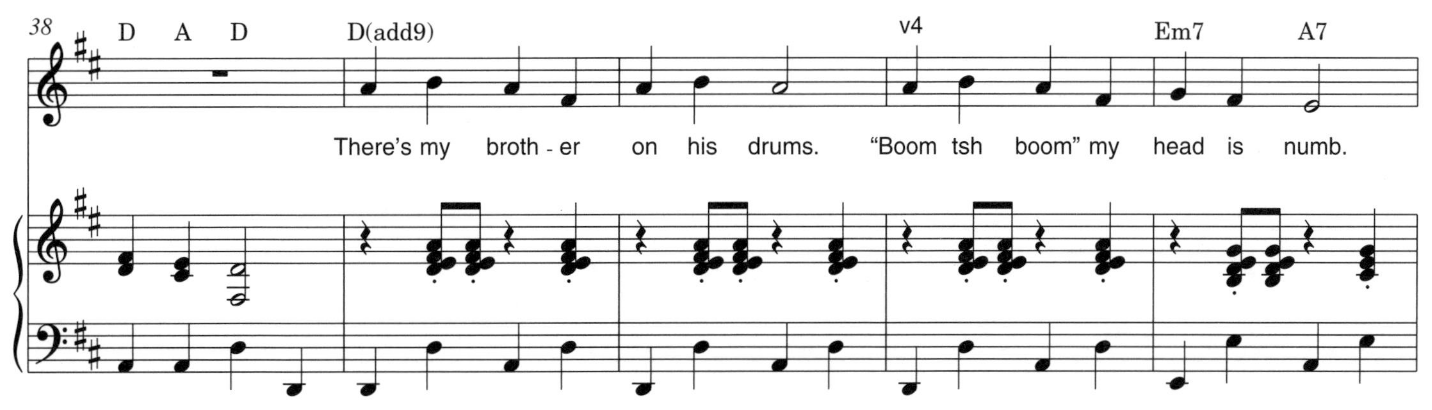
38
D A D
D(add9)
v4
Em7
A7
There's my broth - er on his drums. "Boom tsh boom" my head is numb.

v3
43
D(add9)
Em7
A7
v2
D(add9)
Em7
A7
"Love ya ba - by" makes me laugh! Miaow, miaow, miaow, well fan - cy that!

v1
47
D(add9)
Em7
A7
CHORUS
D
Bm
G
D
G
A7sus4
Rat-a-tat - tat it goes once more. When I lis-ten then I can see what a noi - sy house this

52
D A7 D
G
A7
D A D
D(add9)
seems to be! Now the clock is chim - ing eight.

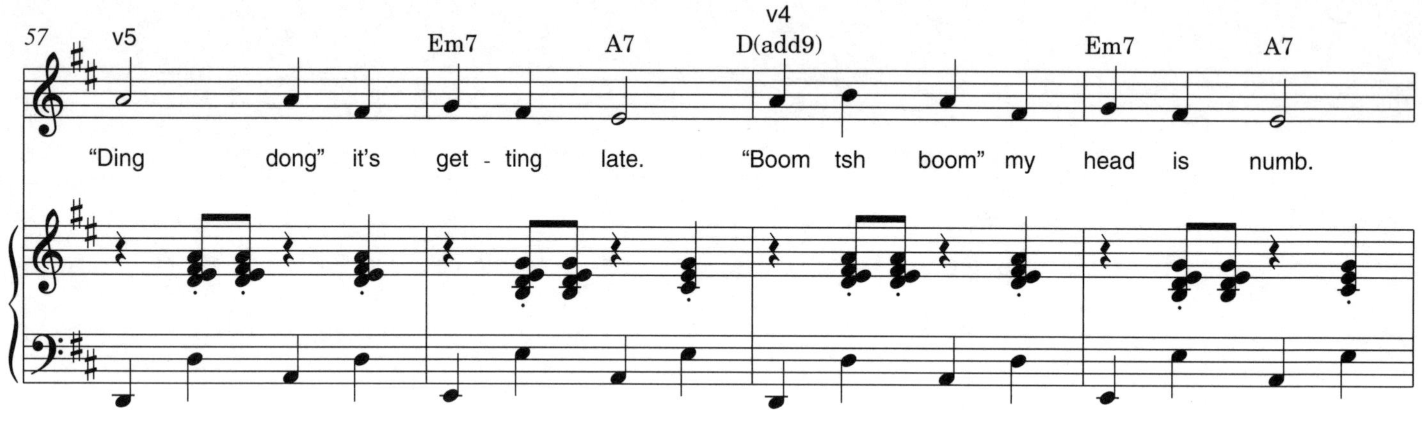
57
v5
Em7
A7
v4
D(add9)
Em7
A7
"Ding dong" it's get - ting late. "Boom tsh boom" my head is numb.

61
v3
D(add9)
Em7
A7
v2
D(add9)
Em7
A7
"Love ya ba - by" makes me laugh! Miaow, miaow, miaow, well fan - cy that!

65
v1
D(add9)
Em7
A7
CHORUS
D
Bm
G
D
G
A7sus4
Rat - a - tat - tat it goes once more. When I lis - ten then I can see what a noi - sy house this

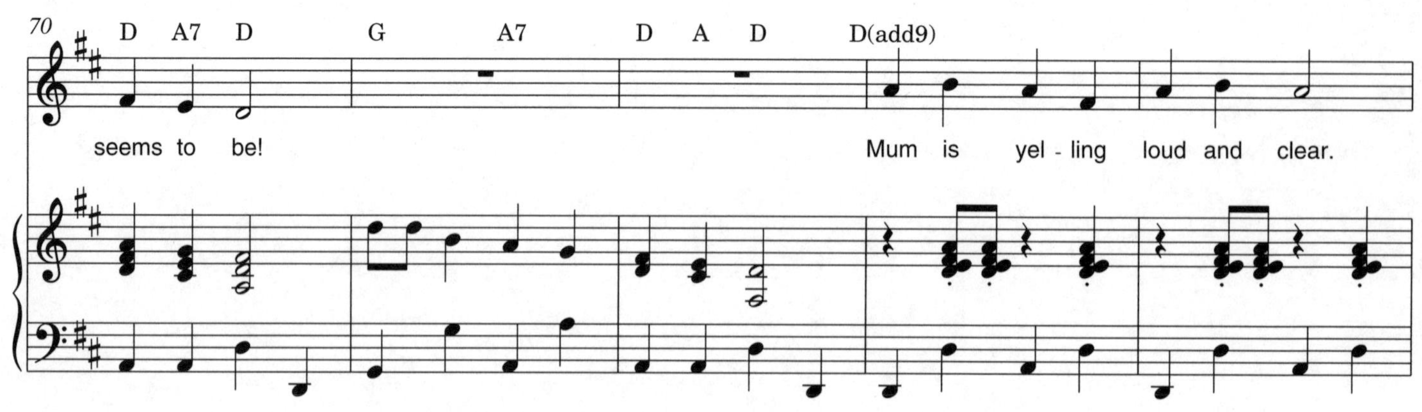
70
D A7 D
G
A7
D A D
D(add9)
seems to be! Mum is yel - ling loud and clear.

75 v6 Em7 A7 v5 D(add9) Em7 A7

"Time for bed" I think I hear. "Ding dong" it's get - ting late.

79 v4 D(add9) Em7 A7 v3 D(add9) Em7 A7

"Boom tsh boom" my head is numb. "Love ya ba - by" makes me laugh!

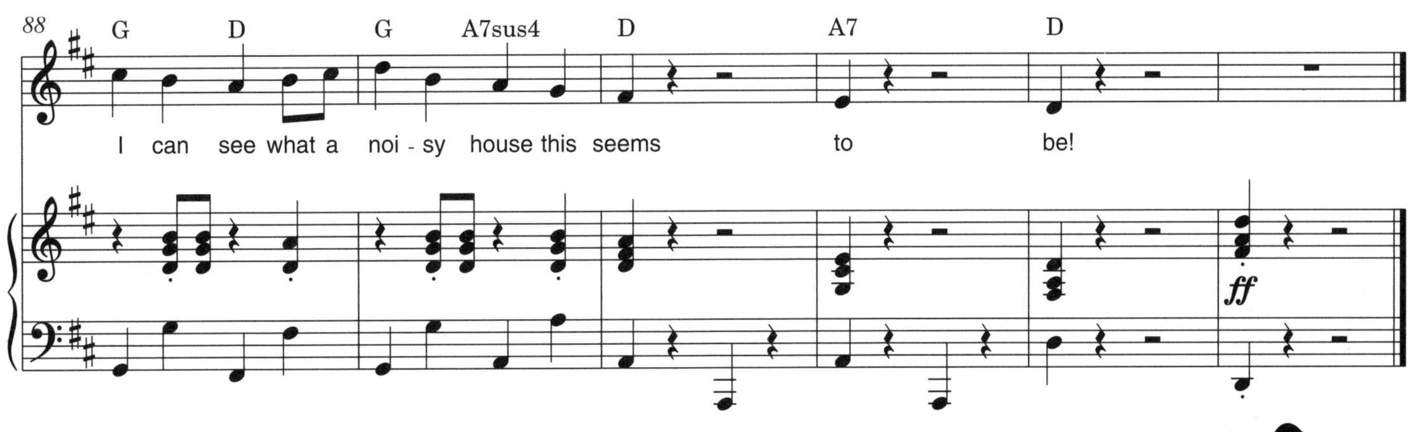

- *Are you using lots of different voices when you make all the noises in the house?*
- *What kind of face will you wear as you sing each different verse?*
- *Are you remembering the rests in the last line of the song?*

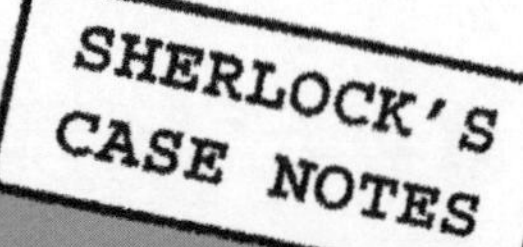

- *Ask the children to close their eyes and listen to the noises they hear around the school. Then ask them to think about the noises they might hear when they go home.*
- *This is a cumulative song where the new sound is added first, so that each verse ends with "Rat-a-tat-tat".*
- *Begin by teaching the children the chorus.*
- *Next teach the verses, but do not try to teach the whole song in one session. Start with the first three verses, and then add a new verse each time.*
- *To help them remember the order of the verses you could ask different children to represent each of the characters and sounds, eg postman, cat, sister, brother, clock and Mum. The children could also hold up pictures or props at the appropriate time.*
- *On the opening words of the chorus "When I listen then I can see" the children may strain or shout to sing the large interval (an octave leap). Warm-ups such as* Wesley Bear's Day at the Office (page 9) *will help them find their higher vocal register.*

Wannabe

Sue Nicholls

13
B♭ E♭ F7 B♭ B♭
wan-na be a drum - mer with a shin - y red kit! I'd play with each
wan-na be a sin - ger and be on T V! I'd war - ble in
wan-na be a con - duc - tor con - duct - ing the band, With play - ers per -
18
Gm C7 F C7 F
rock band and be a great hit!
op' - ra and make a C D! I will make my for - tune,
- form - ing to ev' - ry com - mand!
23
C7 F E♭ Gm F7 B♭
just you wait and see! I'll be a mu-si-cal ce - le - bri - ty!
29
E♭ Gm F7 B♭ E♭ Gm
Dum ch ch, dum ch ch, dum ch ch, dum ch ch! Dum ch ch! Dum ch ch,
Ah ha ha, ah ha ha, ah ha ahhhhh! Ah ha ha, ah ha ha,
One two three, one two three, one two three, one two three! One two three, one two three,

35
F7 Bb Bb F Bb F repeat x 3

dum ch tsssssss! I
ah ha ahhhhhh!
one two three, one two three!

41
Bb Eb F7 Bb

wan - na be, wan - na be a mu - si - cal star! Let's

45
Bb Eb F Bb

hope the world is rea - dy for me: da, da, da, da, Dah!

- *Are you using different voices for each musical star?*
- *Are you beating in time with the music when you sing about the conductor?*
- *Are you acting the part of the drummer, opera singer and conductor?*
- *Are you acting like a superstar when you sing "Dah dah dah dah" in the introductory verse and at the end of the song?*

SHERLOCK'S CASE NOTES

- *You could set the scene of the song by talking about programmes on television like* Britain's Got Talent *and* X Factor. *Ask the children what they want to be when they grow up.*
- *Begin by teaching the children the repeated line of the main verses, "I will make my fortune" etc.*
- *Next teach them verses 1, 2 and 3. Teach the introductory verse "I wannabe, wannabe a musical star!" last. This is also sung again at the end of the song.*
- *Encourage the children to use different vocal qualities, eg for the musical star use a 'twangy' voice and for the singer use an 'opera' voice.*
- *The children may confuse the tune of the introductory verse "I wannabe, wannabe a musical star" with the tune of the other verses "I wannabe a drummer". Patterning the shape of the music with your hands will help them remember which melody to sing.*

My Birthday Party

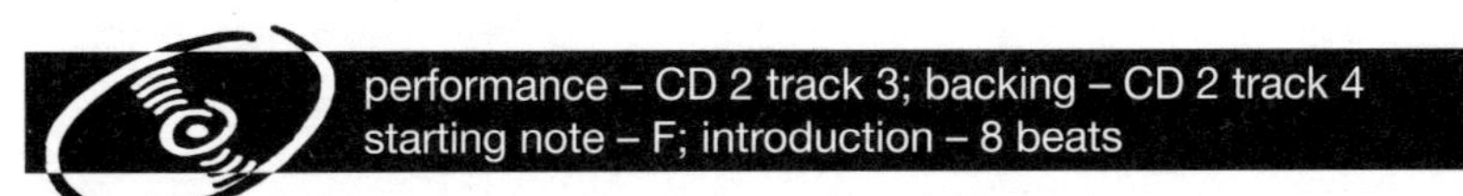
performance – CD 2 track 3; backing – CD 2 track 4
starting note – F; introduction – 8 beats

Kaye Umansky

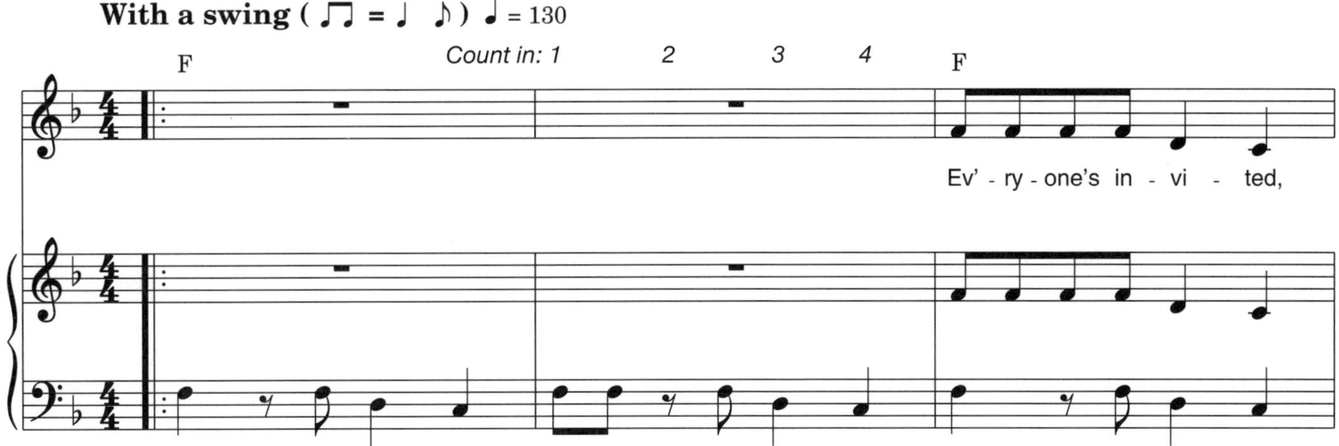
With a swing
= 130
Count in: 1 2 3 4
F
F
Ev' - ry - one's in - vi - ted,

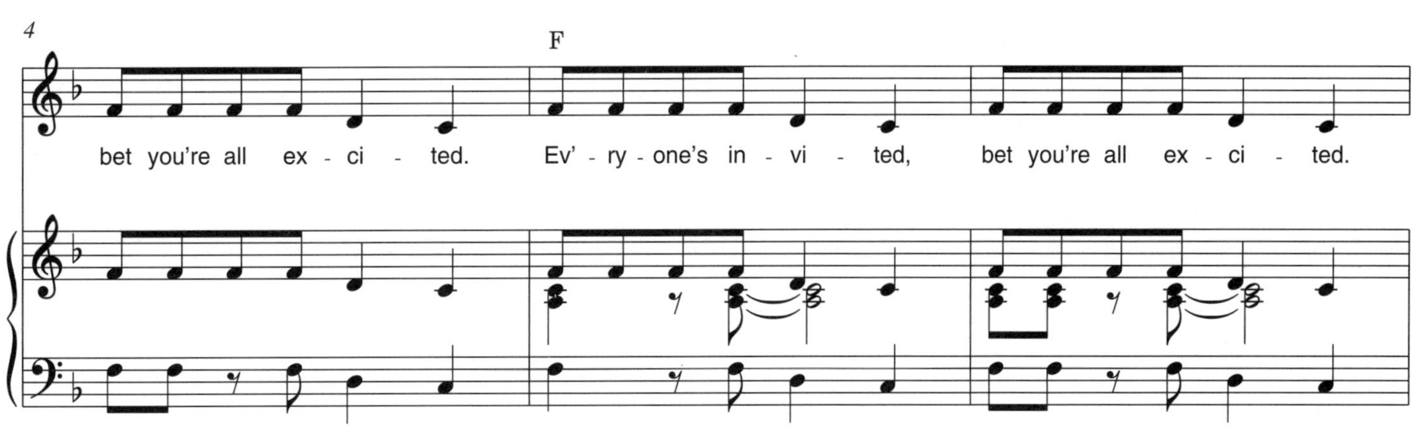
4
F
bet you're all ex - ci - ted. Ev' - ry - one's in - vi - ted, bet you're all ex - ci - ted.

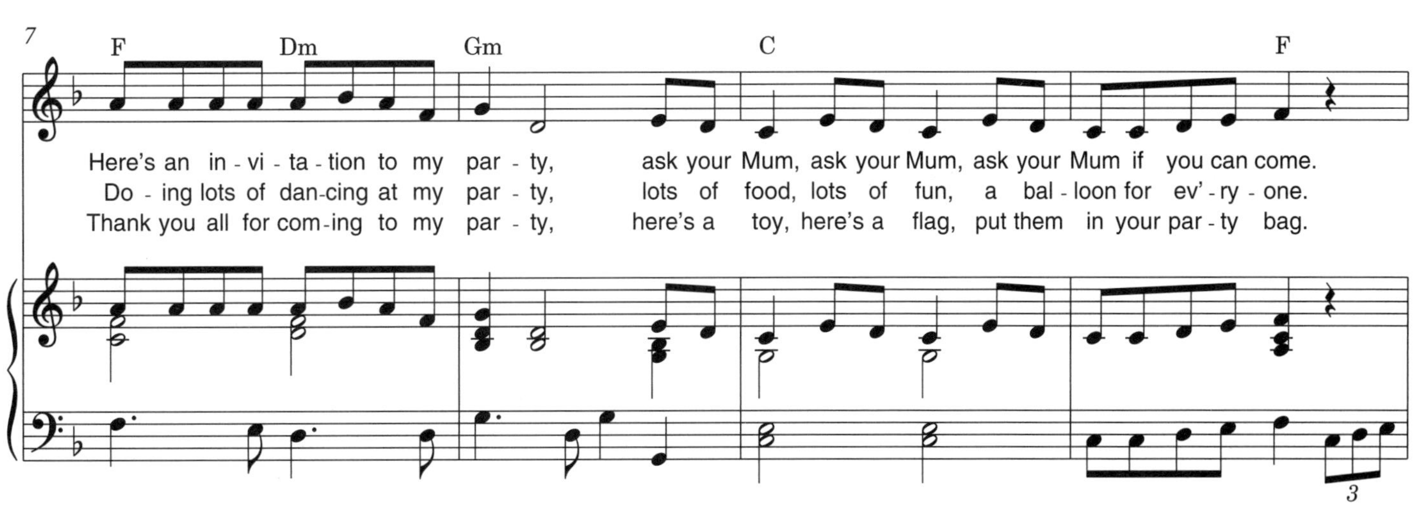
7
F Dm Gm C F
Here's an in - vi - ta - tion to my par - ty, ask your Mum, ask your Mum, ask your Mum if you can come.
Do - ing lots of dan-cing at my par - ty, lots of food, lots of fun, a bal - loon for ev' - ry - one.
Thank you all for com-ing to my par - ty, here's a toy, here's a flag, put them in your par - ty bag.
3

11
F Dm Gm C F B♭ C
Here's an in - vi - ta - tion to my par - ty, to - day at half past three. Ev'-ry-one loves a
Do - ing lots of dan-cing at my par - ty, to - day at half past three. Ev'-ry-one loves a
Thank you all for com-ing to my par - ty, to - day at half past three. Ev'-ry-one loved my
16
Am Dm Gm C7 F B♭ C Am Dm
par - ty, hope you come a - long to jump and shout and blow the can-dles out and
par - ty, hope you come a - long to jump and shout and blow the can-dles out and
birth - day, glad you came a - long to jump and shout and blow the can-dles out and
21
1.2 3
C F C F Dm
sing the hap-py birth - day song. sing the hap-py birth - day song.
sing the hap-py birth - day song.
23
C C C F
sing the hap-py birth - day, sing the hap-py birth - day, sing the hap-py birth - day song!

- Can you show with your voice and face that you are becoming more excited each time you sing the words “Everyone’s invited, bet you’re all excited”?
- Are you remembering that the words of the last chorus are different? How many times do you sing “sing the happy birthday song” to finish?
- Are you looking and smiling at your friend as you give them their party invitation?
- Do you know the date of your own birthday?

SHERLOCK’S CASE NOTES

- *Talk to the children about being invited to their friend’s birthday party. Who do they have to ask if they are allowed to go?*
- *Sing or play the song to the children. Ask them to listen out for how many times they have to ask their Mum?* (Bars 8, 9 and 10)
- *You could add simple actions to the song as follows:*

  “Here’s an invitation” – turn to your neighbour and pretend to exchange invitation cards
  “Today at half past three” – point to imaginary watches
  “Jump and shout” – do a little jump and then cup your hands around your mouth (but make sure it is only one jump!).
- *Before teaching verse 2 ask the children what sort of things they would expect to happen at a birthday party.*

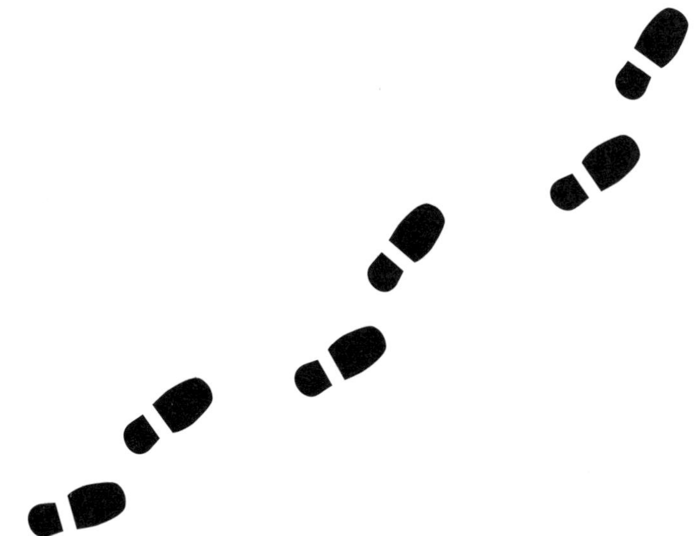

Blame it on Brian

Rebecca Lawrence

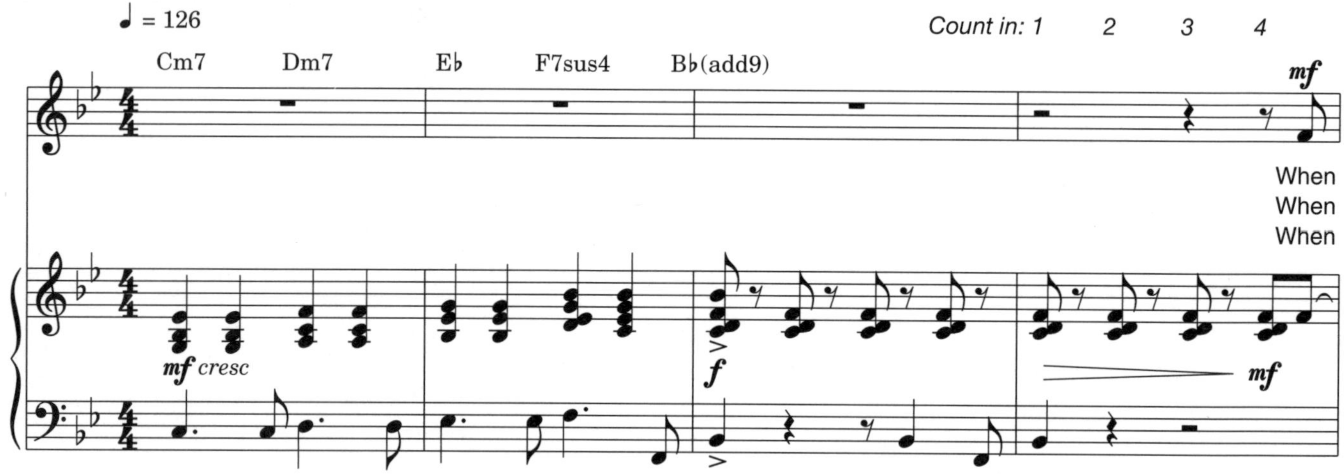

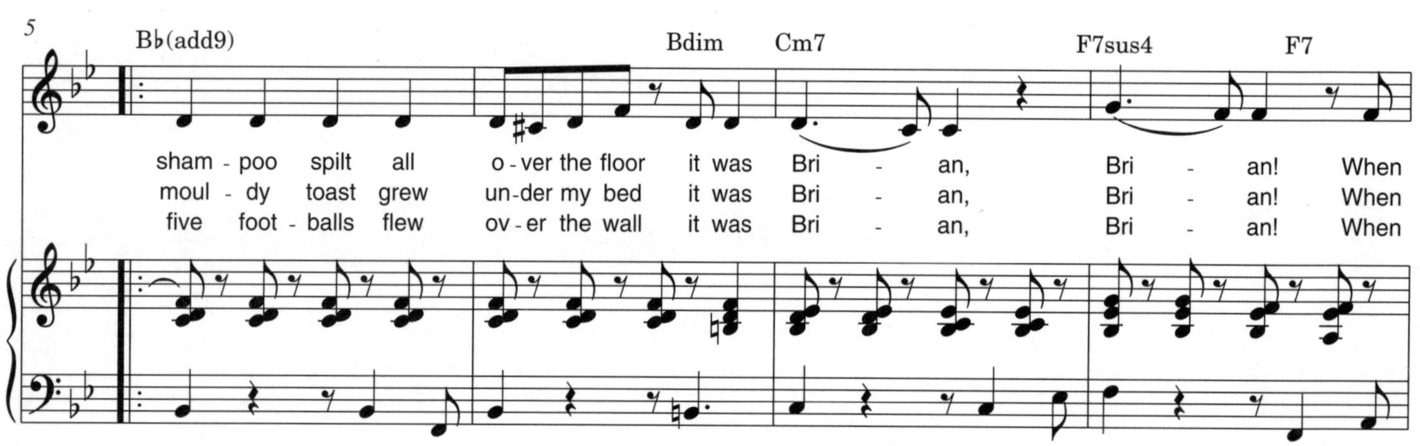

Chorus
13
E♭
Cm
Dm
Dm7
May - be I should tell the truth and get in - to trou - ble, in - stead of blam - ing ev - 'ry - thing on
16
G7
Cm7
cresc
Dm7
E♭
Cm
F7sus4
F7
my naugh - ty dou - ble. It's just too ea - sy to tell a tale on Bri - - - -
cresc
1.2
3
20
B♭(add9)
f
mf
B♭(add9)
mf
E♭
- an! When - an! But sec - ret - ly be - tween
f
mf
mf
22b
Cm
Dm
Dm7
G7
me and you all the things that he did it just is - n't true, for

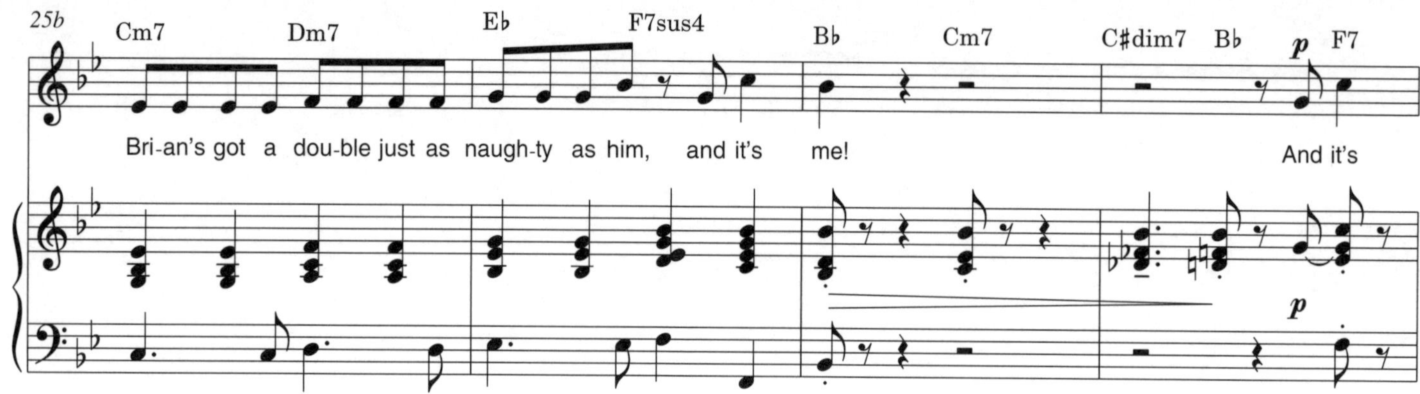

Singing Sherlock wants to know:

- Can you turn up your 'volume control switch' when you sing the chorus "Its just too easy to tell a tale on Brian"?
- Can you make up actions for the different verses like "When pancakes flipped" and "When five footballs flew over the wall"?
- When you sing the last verse can you tell your secret to the audience using your whispering voice? Are you looking very mischievous when you admit to it being you who has done all these naughty things?

SHERLOCK'S CASE NOTES

- *Introduce the song by asking the children if they have ever blamed things that have gone wrong on their brothers or sisters? Do they sometimes have an imaginary friend to blame for all the mishaps when they do not want to own up to things and get told off? In this song we blame it all on our imaginary friend called Brian.*
- *Ask the children to point to an imaginary figure of Brian, to act as a focus point when they sing the word "Brian".*
- *Again words are really important in this song; children need to use their storytelling face to portray the meaning to the audience.*
- *To add vocal variety and interest ask different groups to sing each verse, with everyone joining in the chorus.*

Crop-Eating Crows

Rebecca Lawrence

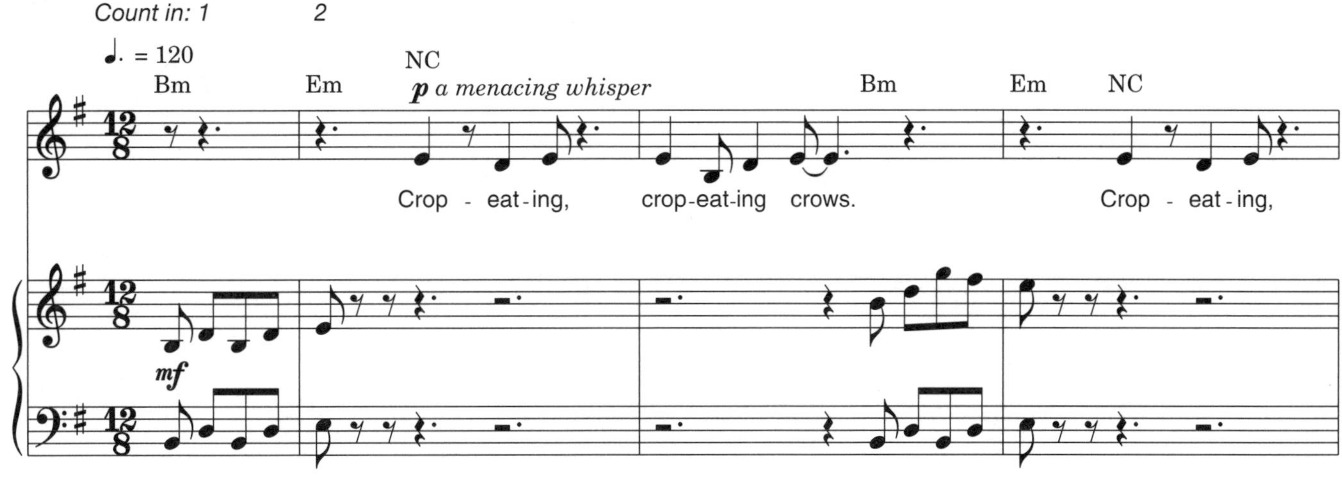

11
E5 NC B7 A7 A7(♯9)
hop-ing _ to scare all the birds . a - way. But they ig - nore me and eat all the crops,
so I ___ can hold my _ arms out wide. Crop - eat - ing, _ crop - eat-ing crows,
I dare you crows to ___ take me on. _ I wave my arms and _ stand my _ ground,
15
B7 A7 F♯m(♭3) B7 E5 NC
1.2
and they just mock me when I tell them to stop. Crop - eat - ing,
crop - eat - ing ___ crop - eat-ing crows. Crop - eat - ing,
and shout out loud __ to the
18
Bm Em B7(♭9) A7 F♯m7(♭5) B7
3
crop-eat-ing crows. Crop - eat-ing, crop-eat-ing crows. crows a - round: "You got - ta
crop-eat-ing crows. Crop - eat-ing, crop-eat-ing crows.
17b
E5 NC Bm Em Dm Em D Em
p mp
STOP EAT-ING, crop-eat-ing crows! STOP EAT-ING, crop-eat-ing crows!

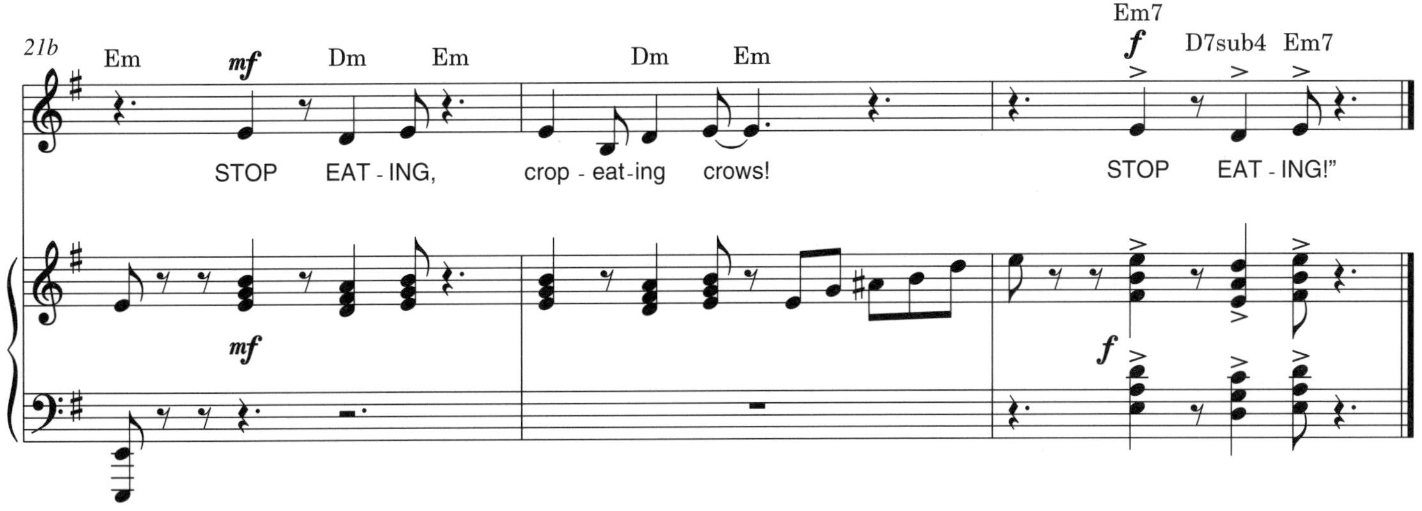

- Are you using your whispering voice when you sing "Crop-eating crows" at the beginning of the song?
- Can you show with your voice and by the way you stand how brave the scarecrow becomes after the farmer stuffs him full of fresh straw?
- Are you using your 'volume control switch' so you get louder each time you sing "Stop eating, crop-eating crows!"?
- Can you make sure you sound the 'p' on the end of the word "crop"? What other words do you think are important to pronounce well?

SHERLOCK'S CASE NOTES

- *Begin by asking the children to describe the scarecrow's job.*
- *To help the children feel the rest, first ask them to tap the pulse while you sing the song (or play the CD track). Next, ask them to clap twice before singing "Crop-eating, crop-eating crows". Then ask the children to use their thinking voices and hear the claps in their heads before they sing.*
- *Make sure the children remember that in the final verse the words change from "Crop-eating crows" to "Stop eating, crop-eating crows".*

When I Was Small

performance – CD 2 track 9; backing – CD 2 track 10
starting note – B; introduction – 12 beats

Rebecca Lawrence

♩ = 112
Count in: 1 2 3
Am7 D Gmaj7 C F♯m7(♭5) B Em Em
mf mischievous
When I was small I'd
I was small I'd
I was small I'd
mf

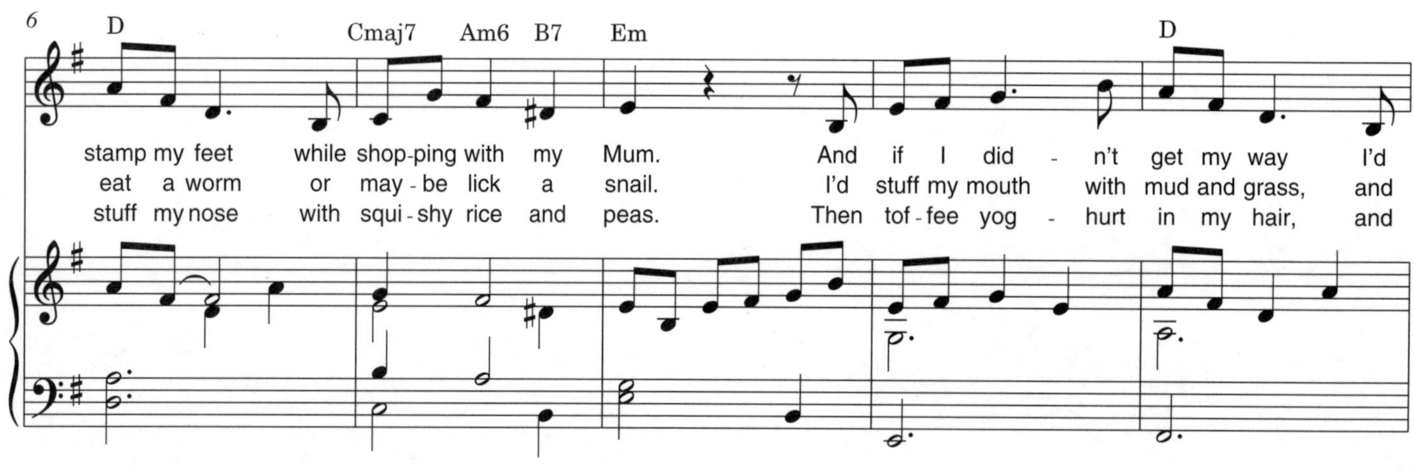
6
D Cmaj7 Am6 B7 Em D
stamp my feet while shop-ping with my Mum. And if I did - n't get my way I'd
eat a worm or may - be lick a snail. I'd stuff my mouth with mud and grass, and
stuff my nose with squi - shy rice and peas. Then tof - fee yog - hurt in my hair, and

11
C Am6 B Esus4 Em E Am7 Dsus4 D G C F♯m7(♭5) Bsus4 B
refined, and somewhat aloof
have a big tan - trum! But now I'm big, I'm sen - si - ble and real - ly ra - ther
dir - ty snow and hail. But now I'm big, I'm sen - si - ble and real - ly ra - ther
baked beans on my knees. But now I'm big, I'm sen - si - ble and real - ly ra - ther

16
E Am7 Dsus4 Am6 B C Em7 Am7 F♯m7(♭5) B7
nice! I shop a - round for qua - li - ty and al - ways check the
good. I on - ly eat the veg - 'ta - bles, as all good gard - 'ners
great. I eat just like the King and Queen, with knife, fork, spoon and
20
1.2
Em F♯m7(♭5) B Em
3
Em E7 Am7 Dsus4 D
price. When plate. Now look at me see
should!
22b
G C F♯m7(♭5) Bsus4 B E Am7 Dsus4 Am6
how I've grown I'm wi - ser, hip and cool! I don't do all those
26b
B C Em7 Am7 F♯m7(♭5) B7 Em
child - ish things, well, not while I'm at school!

- Are the beginnings and endings of all your words really clear, eg "lick a snail", "baked beans" etc, so you can tell the story clearly?
- Can you make the audience laugh when you sing about all the naughty and silly things you did?
- Can you use your posh voice when you sing about being very grown up and sensible?

SHERLOCK'S CASE NOTES

- *Introduce the song by asking the children if they have baby brothers and sisters. What mischievous things do they get up to? Of course, now we are grown up in KS1 we do not do that kind of thing anymore!*
- *The children need to capture the contrast between the two moods of the song – the mischievous toddler and the more sensible child.*
- *It is important that the children observe the rests in the section "But now I'm big, I'm sensible" etc, as this will characterise the more grown-up child.*
- *Make sure the children really enjoy singing the very descriptive words in the songs, eg "tantrum", "squishy rice" and "toffee yoghurt" etc.*
- *In the last verse the children may find "knife, fork, spoon and plate" quite tricky to articulate. Practise slowly or speak the words in a funny voice until they are secure.*
- *Teach this song over a period of time – perhaps adding a new verse in each singing session.*

The Honey Bee

Sue Furlong

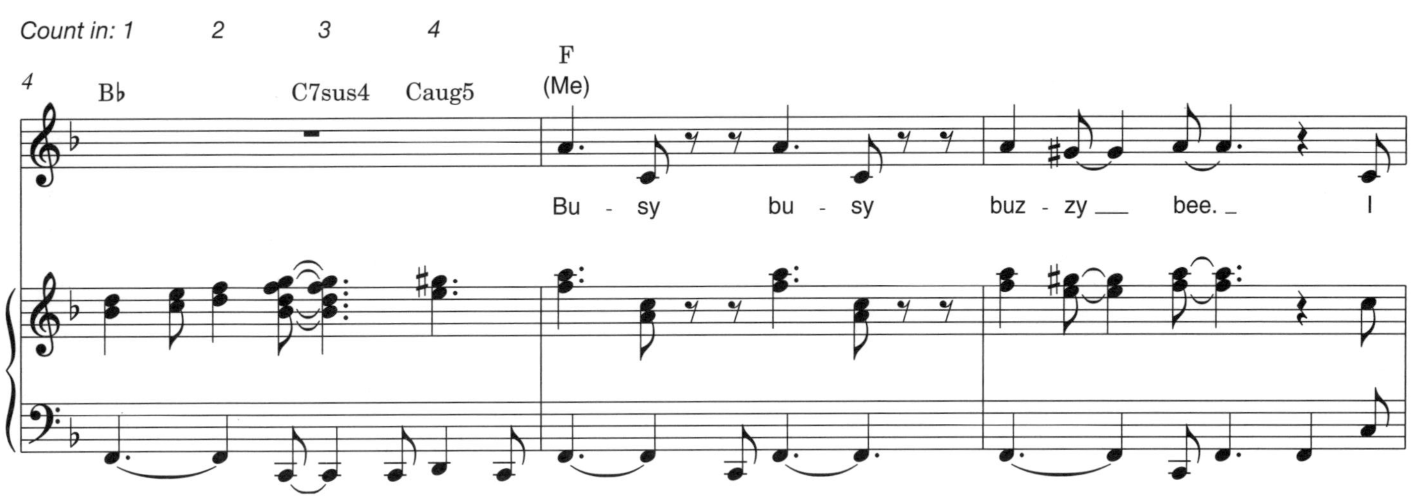

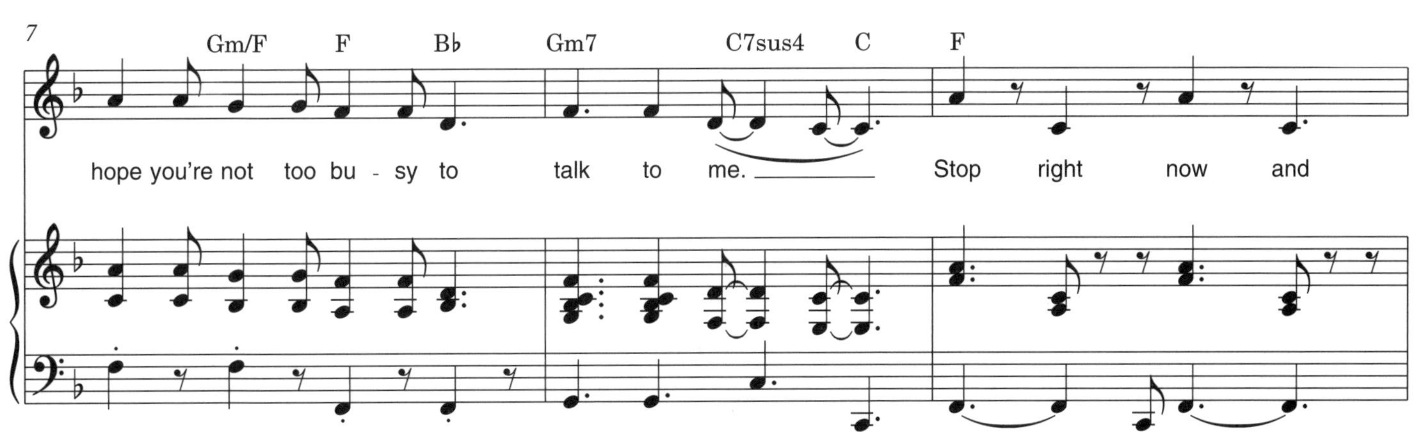

10
Caug5 F Daug5 G7 C7
buzz this __ way, __ I real - ly wan - na know just how was your day? ____
13
F C7 B♭maj7 F(add9)
(Honey Bee)
Oh I saw a lit - tle bun - ny on my jour - ney __ here. ____ I was
16
B♭maj7 F(add9) B♭maj7
buzz - in' in the bush when he said, come __ here. __ Have you an - y run - ny hon - ey for my
19
F(add9) D C7sus4 C7 F Dm7 E
toast, you ___ see, ____ there ain't no car - rots for my tea.

22
F
(Me again)
Bu - sy bu - sy buz - zy bee. I hope you're not too bu - sy to
Gm/F F B♭
25
Gm7 C7sus4 C F
talk to me. Stop right now and buzz this way. I
28
Caug5 F Daug5 G7 C7 F C7
(Honey Bee)
real - ly wan - na know just how was your day? I was
31
B♭maj7 F(add9) B♭maj7
feel - in' kin - da bad 'cos the bun - ny was so sad. You see he had no car - rots for his

34
F(add9)
B♭maj7
F(add9)
D
tea.
So I emp - tied out the sack that I have on my back.
I
37
C7sus4
C7
F
Dm7
D7
G
(Me)
gave him run - ny hon - ey for his tea.
Bu - sy bu - sy
40
Am/G
G
C
Am7
D7sus4
D
buz - zy bee.
I hope you're not too bu - sy to talk to me.
43
G
Daug5
G
Eaug5
Stop right now and buzz this way.
I real - ly wan - na know just

- Can you make the 'b' and 'z' sounds on the words "busy" and "buzzy" very clear and absolutely together?
- Can you remember the different ending to the song?
- When you sing "I really wanna know just how was your day?", is your neck long and tall like a giraffe?
- Can you feel a buzz on the tip of your tongue as you buzz like the bee at the end of the song?

SHERLOCK'S CASE NOTES

- *This song is perhaps the most difficult in the book, and is also suitable for Years 3 and 4.*
- *Explain to the children that the rabbit in the song has a problem, and he asks the Honey Bee to help him out.*
- *The opening notes "Busy, busy" and "Stop right now"* (bars 5 and 9) *have a large interval that the children may find tricky. If the children tend to slide between the two notes ask them to make each note very short, then gradually lengthen the first note.*
- *The octave leaps at "there ain't no carrots"* (bar 20) *also need care. Ask the children to pattern the notes in the air, making sure they only move their hands up and down and not their whole body.*
- *Beware, the children may confuse the melody of the final "I really wanna know". You will need to teach this accurately* (bars 45–46).
- *This could be performed in two groups – one singing the part of Me and the other group singing the part of the Honey Bee. Both groups can join together to sing the final "Busy, busy" etc, after the key change* (bar 39).

Sherlock in Concert

Animal Magic and *Pinocchio Songs* are suitable for Year 2 and lower Keystage 2. Younger children may be able to sing some of these songs depending on their previous vocal experience. The songs can be sung either as medleys or as individual items in a concert. They lend themselves well to movement, actions or simple gestures.

Songs

"I wannabe, wannabe a musical star!"

The performance starts from the moment you walk onto the stage or performance area

- Walk tall and stand proud
- Do not wave at your Mum and Dad
- Be audience-friendly at all times – smile as you walk on stage, between songs, and during the applause

Tell the story

Think about what kind of face you need to wear for each song you sing.

Remember you are all part of a singing team – each one of you is important! :) x

Before the song starts can you imagine you are a high-quality fish finger? No fidgeting, looking at your friend or shuffling your feet. Make sure you are looking at your conductor or teacher.

And now ... the performance!
I hope the world is ready for me, da da da da da ...

I'm a Giraffe

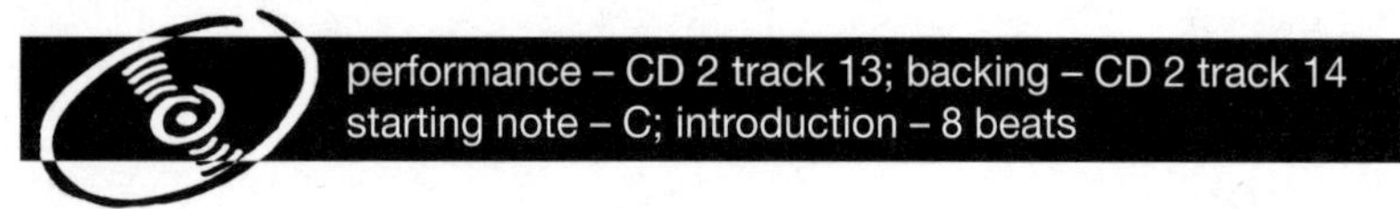

Rebecca Lawrence

12
F Gm C7 F Gm7 F B♭
do? How d'you do? It's ve - ry nice to see you pas - sing through! Hel - lo! Hel - lo.
do? How d'you do? It's ve - ry nice to see you pas - sing through! Hel - lo! Hel - lo.
do? How d'you do? It's ve - ry nice to see you pas - sing through! Hel - lo! Hel - lo.
16
F F7 D Gm F C7 F
do? How d'you do? I hope you liked your day at the zoo!
do? How d'you do? I hope you liked your day at the zoo!
do? How d'you do? I hope you liked your day at the zoo!

SHERLOCK'S CASE NOTES

- *This song is a child's conversation with different animals at the zoo. To help the children portray the different characters, in the chorus ask one half of the class to sing the animal part and the other half to sing the child's response.*
- *You could also do this with the children facing each other in pairs. Making eye contact with a partner as you sing (as you would if you were having a spoken conversation with another person) is an important skill. Children, and indeed adults, can find this difficult. Initially children may react by being silly or giggly, but persevere!*
- *For the verses you could divide the class into three groups, each group taking the character of one of the animals. This also gives opportunities for the children to sing in smaller groups* (see 'Go solo', page 33).
- *Ask the children to choose their own actions for the line "cool and hip and funky".*

Singing Sherlock wants to know:

- *Is your neck nice and tall like a giraffe's?*
- *Are you able to use two different voices, one for the animal and one for the child? What kind of voice will you use for the child, giraffe, camel and monkey?*
- *Are you making a nice 'oo' shape on the words "do", "through" and "zoo"?*

Tiger Tango

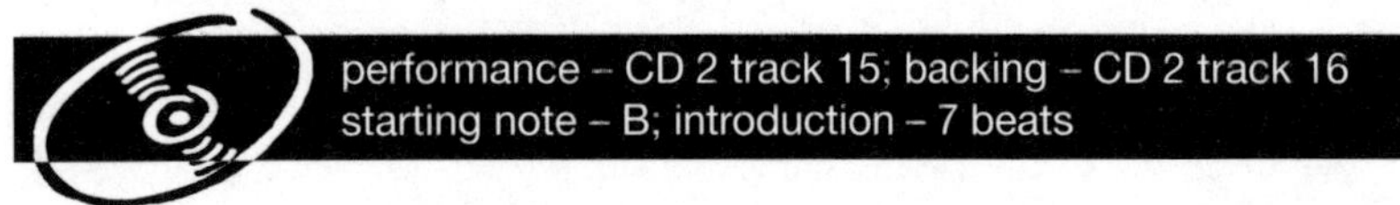
performance – CD 2 track 15; backing – CD 2 track 16
starting note – B; introduction – 7 beats

Rebecca Lawrence

Count in: 1 2 3

With passion! ♩ = 126
Em
mf
Bsus4 B
Oh yes we dance, the Ti-ger Tan-go. We're in a
f
mf

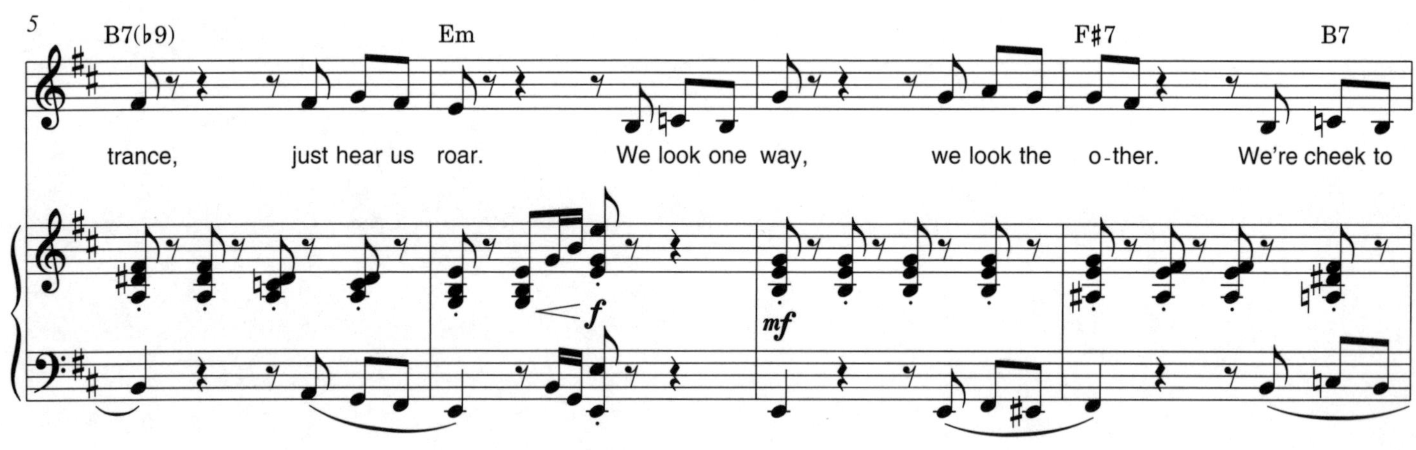
5
B7(♭9)
Em
F#7
B7
trance, just hear us roar. We look one way, we look the o-ther. We're cheek to
f
mf

9
F#m7(♭5)
B7(♭9)
Em
D
G
D
f
cheek, and paw to paw. O - lé! We love to dance, we love to move.
f

13
Em7
A7
D
D7
D7aug
G
F#m
F#7
Bm7
We love to spin, we love to groove. Let all the rhy-thms move your feet,
17
Em
A7
D
G
D
Lilting ♩=♩
G6
A
G
A7
D
G
D
mf legato
and bring a-live the dan-cing beat, O-lé!
I'm just a
mf legato
mp
24
Em
A
A7
D
A
G
A
D
wal-la-by try-ing to waltz, keep-ing my feet on the ground.
One, two, three,
32
G
G#dim
D
A7
Bm
A
D
D7
C
D7
G
f
one, two, three it's not that hard, but I'd ra-ther be bounc ing-a-round.
Boing!
We love to

40
D
Em
A7 G A7 D
D7 C D7
dance, we love to move. We love to spin, we love to groove.
47
G
A7
F♯m
F♯7
Bm
G6
E7
A Bm7 A7 D
G D
Let all the rhy - thms move your feet, and bring a - live the dan - cing beat.
Bouncy ♩ = ♩
55
Em7
A
D G D
mf
G
A7
D
I'm at the hedge-hog hoe-down, now watch out for my spines. We
f
mf
59
E7
A7
D
gal - lop down the barn-yard, we try to keep in lines. We do - si-do in dan-ger with

62 G G#dim7 D A7sus4 A7 D Em D7

prick-les on our back, with a 'Hey down, hoe down, hey down, hoe down you'll soon get the knack! Yee-ha!'

65 G D Em7 A7 D D7

We love to dance, we love to move. We love to spin, we love to groove.

69 G Em F#m F# Bm G Em7 A A7 D G D

Let all the rhy-thms move your feet, and bring a-live the dan - cing beat.

8

- *Are you standing tall and proud as if you are about to dance the tango?*
- *Are you able to sing smoothly and get the different style for the* Wallaby Waltz*?*
- *Can you make your voice go from low to high on the word "boing"?*
- *Can you slap your thighs in time to the music as if you were at a barn dance?*
- *Can you use your cowboy voice for the* Hedgehog Hoedown*?*
- *Are you remembering to put a 'h' on the beginning of "Hey down, hoe down"?*

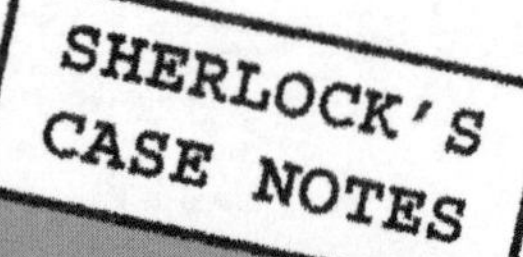

- *In the* Tiger Tango *be aware that some children may find the pickup notes "Oh yes we dance" quite low, and may need to speak-sing. This is fine, as the notes do not linger too long in this register.*
- *To create the right tango feel the rests need to be observed correctly. Initially, children may find this difficult; ask them to make a movement or action in the rest. Remember, nobody should be singing whilst performing the action. For example, the children could move their heads to the right in the rest after the words "We look one way", and to the left in the rest after "we look the other way". In the rest after "cheek to cheek" they could touch their right, then left cheek. Similarly in the rest after "paw to paw" they could hold out their right hand and then their left.*
- *Words such as "dance", "trance", "roar", "way", "other" etc are all short and need to be crisp and clear.*
- *To help the children internalise the waltz time of* Wallaby Waltz *ask them to sway from side to side on the strong beat of each bar –* **one***, two, three,* **one***, two, three etc. This will also help them not to rush.*
- *Because* Hedgehog Hoedown *rattles along at quite a speed teach it in small sections and very slowly. Speak the words rhythmically before singing them, gradually adding each section together.*

The Dolphin Song

performance – CD 2 track 17; backing – CD 2 track 18
starting note – D; introduction – 18 beats

Rebecca Lawrence

♩ = 72
Ocean drum, clicks, whistles
p

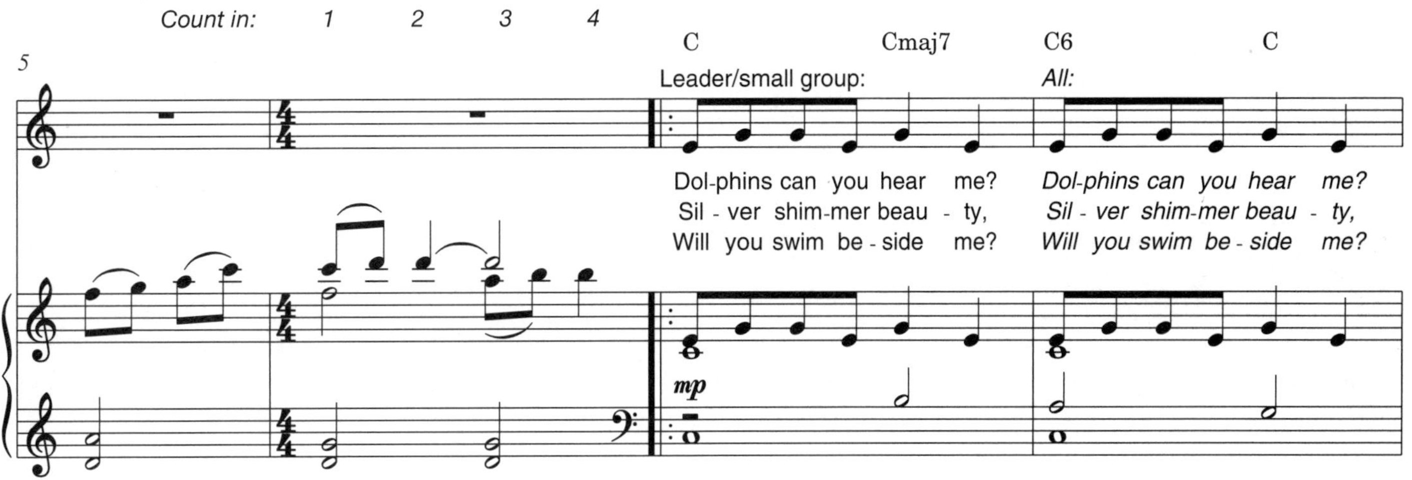
5
Count in: 1 2 3 4
C
Cmaj7
C6
C
Leader/small group:
All:
Dol-phins can you hear me?
Sil - ver shim-mer beau - ty,
Will you swim be - side me?
Dol-phins can you hear me?
Sil - ver shim-mer beau - ty,
Will you swim be - side me?
mp

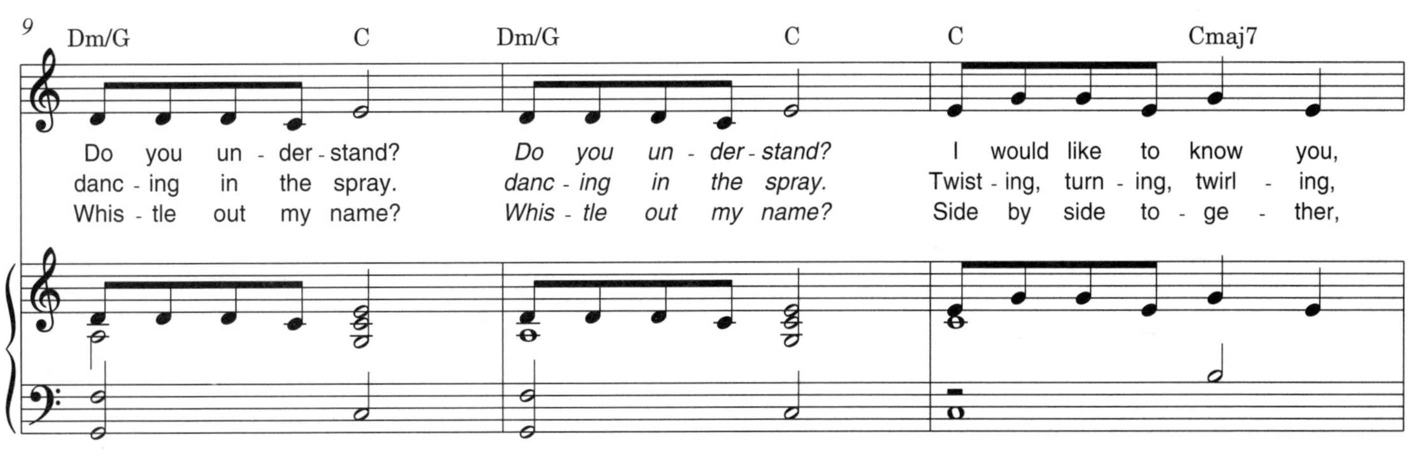
9
Dm/G
C
Dm/G
C
C
Cmaj7
Do you un - der - stand?
danc - ing in the spray.
Whis - tle out my name?
Do you un - der - stand?
danc - ing in the spray.
Whis - tle out my name?
I would like to know you,
Twist - ing, turn - ing, twirl - ing,
Side by side to - ge - ther,

12
C6 C Dm/G C Dm/G C B♭/C All:
I would like to know you, but I must live on land. but I must live on land.
Twist-ing turn-ing twirl-ing, an o-cean blue bal-let. an o-cean blue bal-let. Your
Side by side to-ge-ther, our mo-tions are the same. our mo-tions are the same.
15
F Em Dm7 F/C C Dm7 F/C
rit
mf
grace and beau-ty com-forts me like an-gels of the sea. You dive so deep you leap so high, you
18
Dm7 Dm/G G7 3rd time to
a tempo
Dm/G C
kiss the moon-light touch the sky.
"Kick, Kick", "Whoosh!"
"Splash!", etc
mp
22
Leader/small group: All:
C Cmaj7 C6 C Dm/G C Dm/G C
Dol-phins can you hear me? Dol-phins can you hear me? Do you un-der-stand? Do you un-der-stand?

rit
26
C
Cmaj7
C6
C
Dm/G
C
Dm/G
C
I would like to know you, *I would like to know you,* but I must live on land. *but I must live on land.*
Ocean drum clicks and whistles
rit

Singing Sherlock wants to know:

- What face are you going to wear when you ask the dolphin all the different questions?
- Are you imagining you are having a real conversation with the dolphin? Are you singing gently to him?
- Can you take out your magic singing paintbrush and give certain words a little extra brush stroke? For example, "**S**ilver **sh**immer beauty", "Your grace and beauty **c**omforts me", and "**Tw**isting, **t**urning, **tw**irling".
- Are you all sounding the 'd' together on the words "understand" and "land"?

SHERLOCK'S CASE NOTES

- *Experiment with different ways of performing this song, eg*

  Verse 1: sung by teacher/leader and echoed by the whole class
  Verse 2: divide the class into two groups; one group leads, the other echoes
  Verse 3: class leads, soloist echoes
  Verse 4: child leads, class echoes

- *Give the children time to breath after* "leap so high" (bar 17) *before they sing the phrase* "kiss the moonlight, touch the sky" (bars 18–19). *Ask them to trace a rainbow shape in the air with their finger. This will help them sing through the phrase and prevent them from running out of breath.*

- *To enhance the atmosphere of the song add vocal sound effects (clicks and whistles, whooshes and splashes) and unpitched percussion instruments (eg ocean drum, rainsticks) at the opening of the song and between the chorus and verses.*

Geppetto Made a Puppet

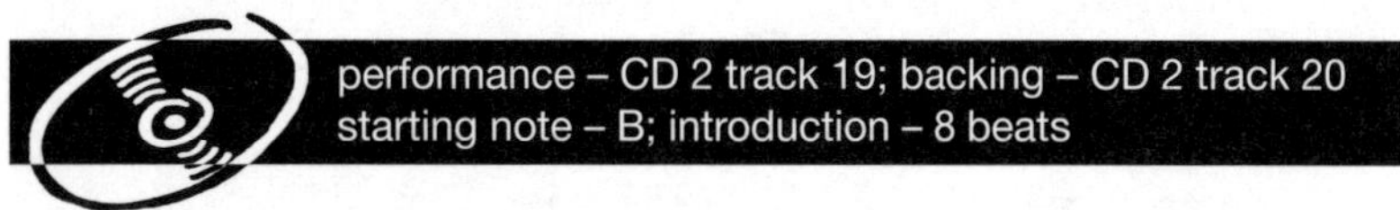
performance – CD 2 track 19; backing – CD 2 track 20
starting note – B; introduction – 8 beats

Lin Marsh

♩ = 100
Count in: 1 2 3 4
A E B7 E
mp
B7sus4 E
Gep - pet - to made a pup-pet, he
mp

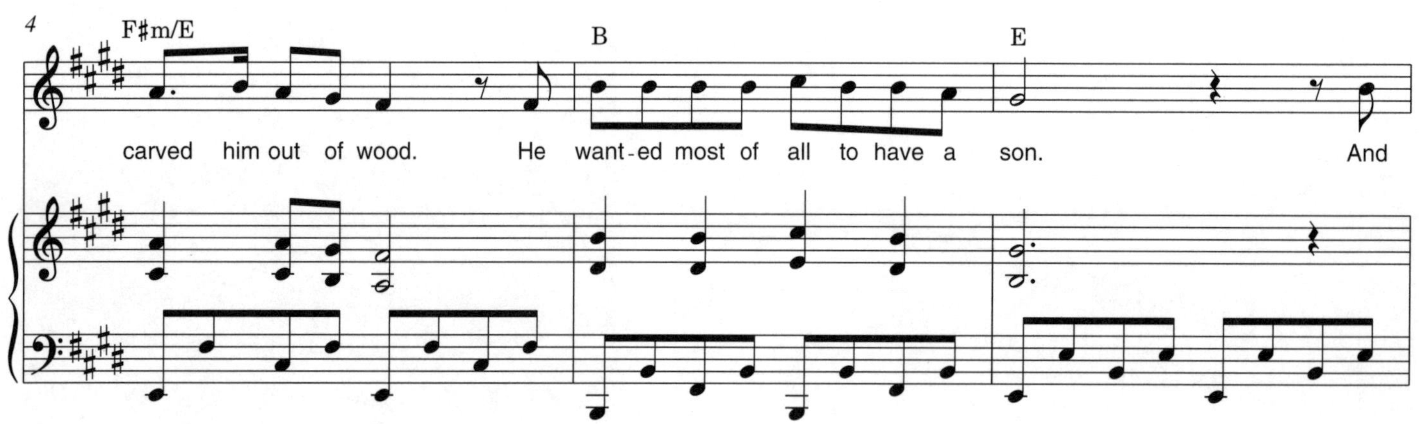
4
F♯m/E
B
E
carved him out of wood. He want-ed most of all to have a son. And

7
B7sus4 E E7
A C♯7 F♯m
B A/B B7
ev' - ry - one could hear him as he ham-mered and he sawed. He worked a-way from dawn till day was

10 E B7sus4 E *mf* A E F♯m7 B7 E

done. With a tap tap here and a tap tap there, the pu - pet was be - gun. But
from fin - gers down to toes. But
came el - bow, knee and chin. But
when came the legs and feet. Pi -

mf

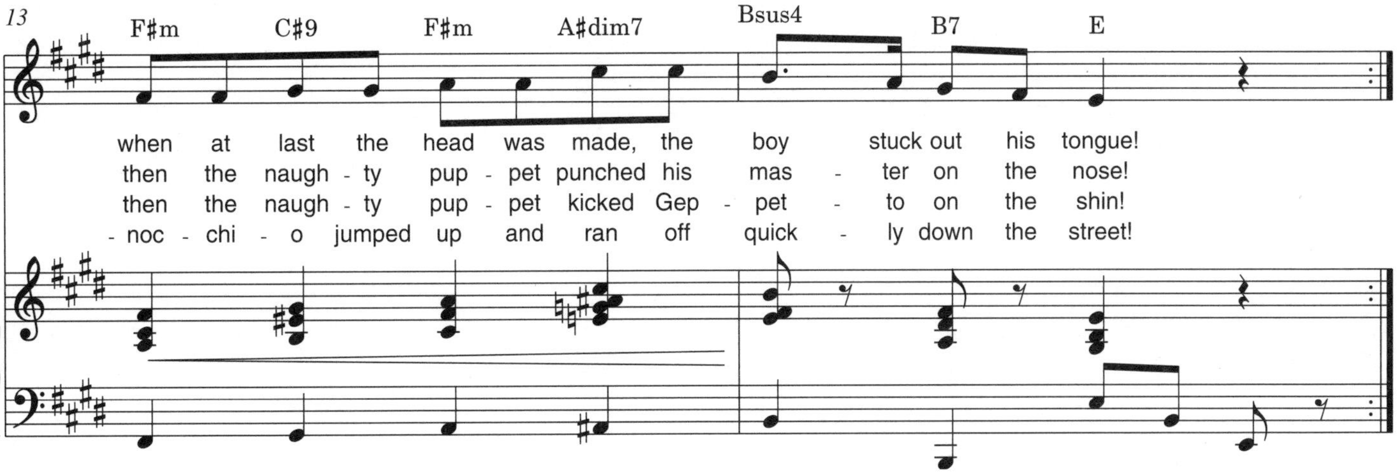

13 F♯m C♯9 F♯m A♯dim7 Bsus4 B7 E

when at last the head was made, the boy stuck out his tongue!
then the naugh - ty pup - pet punched his mas - ter on the nose!
then the naugh - ty pup - pet kicked Gep - pet - to on the shin!
- noc - chi - o jumped up and ran off quick - ly down the street!

- Are you telling the story by making your words very crisp and clear?
- Are you all taking breaths at the same time? For example, "He wanted most of all to have a son" should be in one breath.
- Can you make up actions to the verses that help you remember the words?
- Can you tap your fingers in time and exactly together as you sing the words "With a tap, tap here and a tap, tap there"?

SHERLOCK'S CASE NOTES

- *Make sure the children hold onto the longer notes on 'Son'* (bar 6) *and 'done'* (bar 10).
- *Be careful with the phrase "from dawn till day is done"* (bar 9). *Children may find this quite difficult, so practise this separately and stop on a different note of the phrase each time. You could also use nonsense words or sing with a character voice, eg posh or twangy.*
- *At the upbeat to bar 12, you need to highlight the different words of the pickup beats of each different verse, eg "from fingers", "came elbow" and "when came".*
- *On the 'tap taps' it would be effective to add some claves, or the children could tap two fingers on their hands.*
- *At bar 14 the children could do the appropriate action in the rest after they sing.*

Pinocchio

Lin Marsh

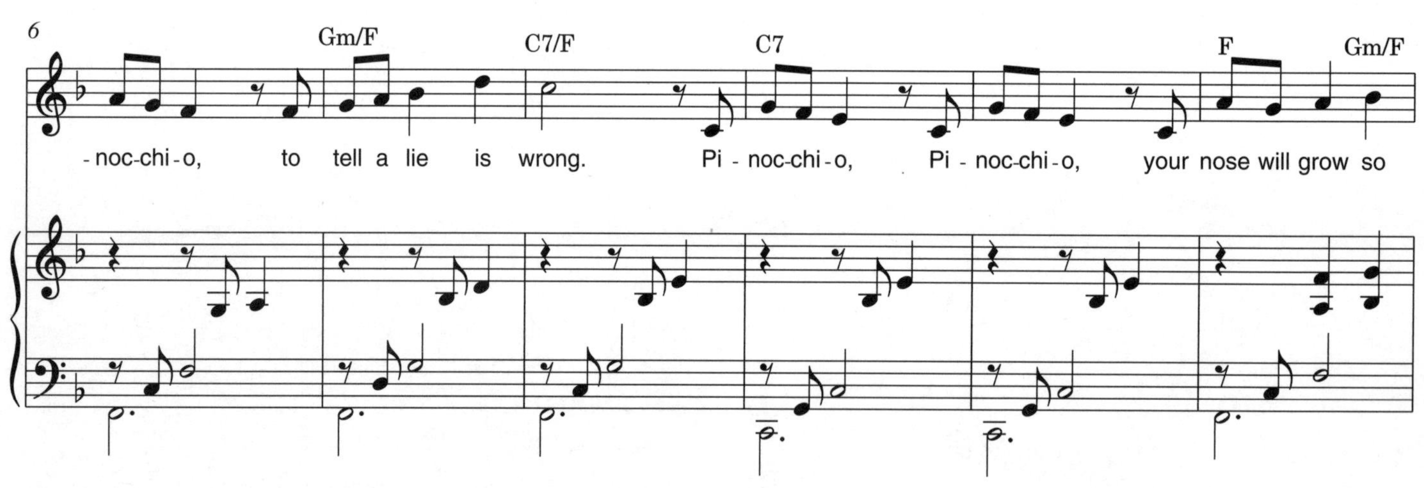

18
Bb(add9) Bb/C C7 F F7 mf Bb(add9) F Gm7 C7
tell the truth, we'll love you all the more. Did you real - ly fight a gi - ant, who lives in the
Are you real - ly rich and fa - mous, a star of the
Do you real - ly own a pal - ace, and live with the
24
F Gm7 C7 F G7
sky? Your nose has grown a lit - tle long - er and we all know
screen? Or is your nose a - bout to tell us it was all a
Queen? Your nose is get - ting quite e - nor - mous big - gest ev - er
CODA
rit
28
C7 repeat x 4 F7 Bb(add9) Bb/C C7 F
why! Pi - noc - chi - o please tell the truth, we'll love you all the more.
dream?
seen!
rit

- *What different faces are you wearing as you tell the story? Can you show you are angry with Pinocchio for telling lies? Can you sound and look shocked as Pinocchio's nose grows bigger?*
- *Can you make up actions for the chorus?*
- *As you sing, can you show with both your face and by the way you stand what it is like to fight a giant, be a rich and famous film star, and live in the Queen's palace?*
- *Are you all watching your teacher/leader carefully so that you all slow down exactly together at the end of the song?*

SHERLOCK'S CASE NOTES

- *Make sure the children keep a tall neck when singing the line "to tell a lie is wrong" as this will help them to reach the word "is" and prevent the phrase from going flat.*
- *Some children may find the downward octave leap on the pickup note after the word "wrong" difficult to pitch. You will need to practise this leap until they are familiar with it.*
- *Make sure the children sustain the pitch through the repeated notes in bar 13 on the words "listen to the fairy" by keeping up the energy and standing tall.*
- *You may like to choose a child to be Pinocchio so that the rest of the children have a focus to sing and react to.*

Down, Down to the Bottom of the Se

performance – CD 2 track 23; backing – CD 2 track 24
starting note – C; introduction – 4 beats

Lin Marsh

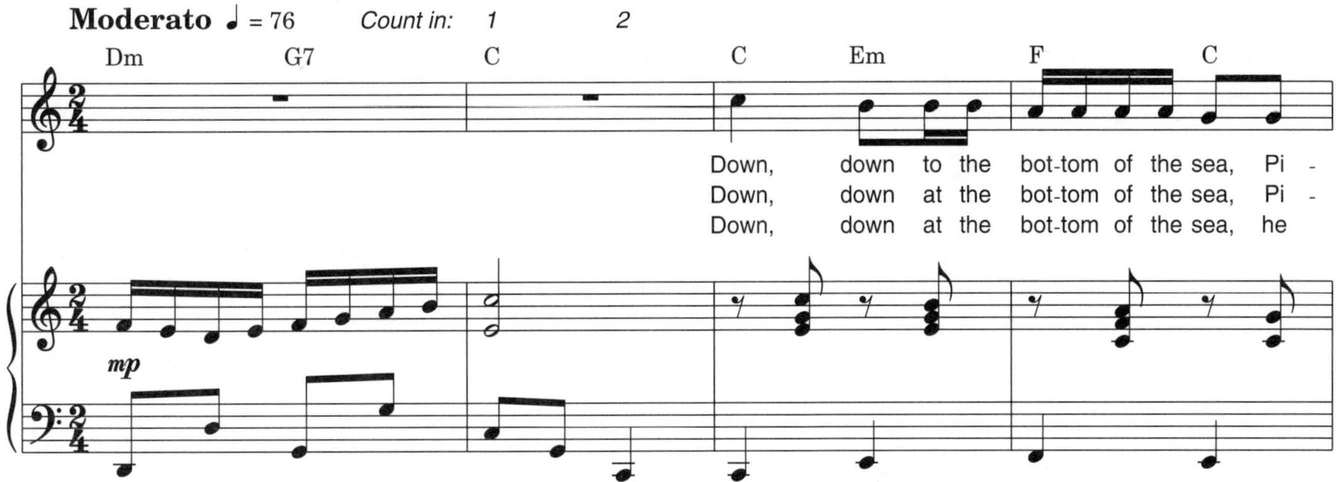
Moderato ♩ = 76
Count in: 1 2
Dm G7 C C Em F C
Down, down to the bot-tom of the sea, Pi -
Down, down at the bot-tom of the sea, Pi -
Down, down at the bot-tom of the sea, he
mp

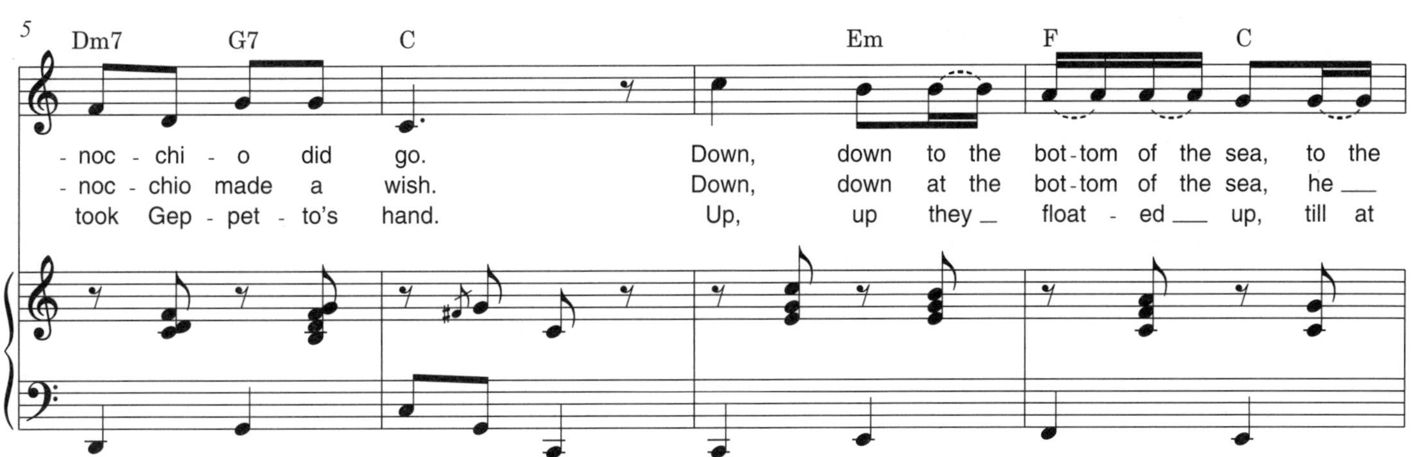
5
Dm7 G7 C Em F C
- noc - chi - o did go. Down, down to the bot-tom of the sea, to the
- noc - chio made a wish. Down, down at the bot-tom of the sea, he
took Gep - pet - to's hand. Up, up they float - ed up, till at

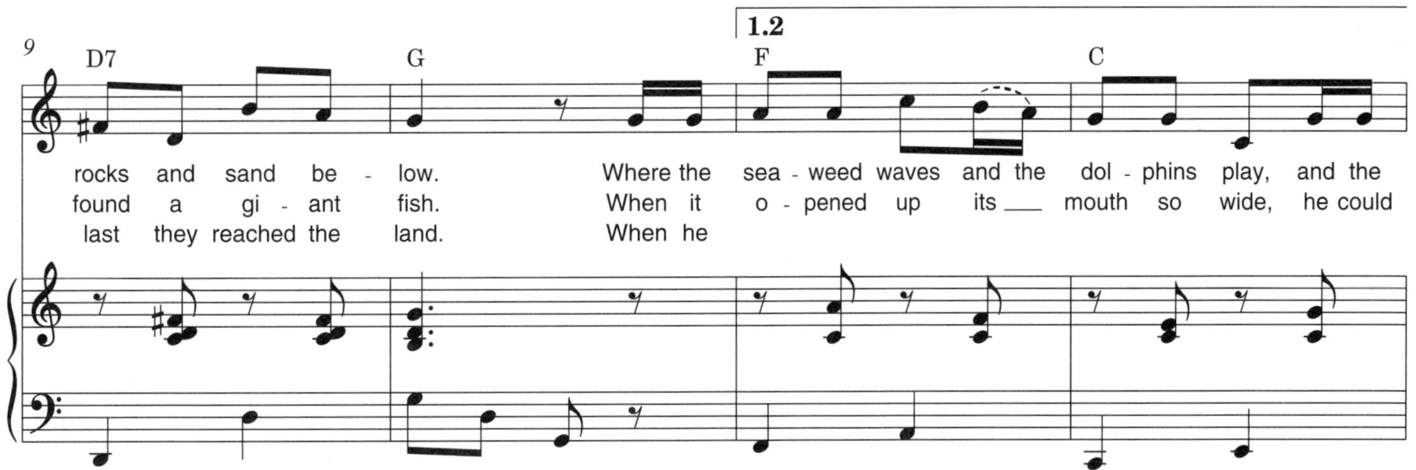
9
1.2
D7 G F C
rocks and sand be - low. Where the sea - weed waves and the dol - phins play, and the
found a gi - ant fish. When it o - pened up its mouth so wide, he could
last they reached the land. When he

(1.2)
13
F F♯dim7 C F♯dim C Em F C
crab and lob - ster hide a - way. Down, down to the bot-tom of the sea, Pi -
see Gep - pet - to deep in - side. Down, down at the bot-tom of the sea, Pi -
(1.2)
3
17
Dm7 G7 C F C
- noc - chi - o did go. looked a - round he smiled with joy, for he'd
- noc - chio made a wish.
13b
F C F F♯dim C Am7 Dm7 G D
turned in - to a real live boy. And hap - py ev - er af - ter they would be.
18b
G C F C Dm7
For in fair - y tales ev' - ry wish comes true. Ev - en when you

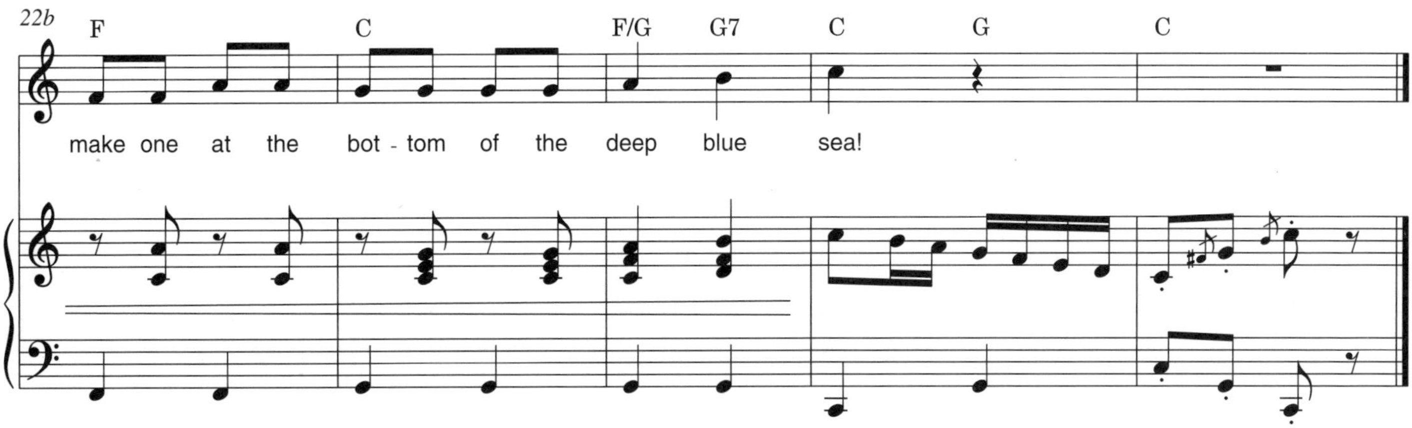
22b
F
C
F/G
G7
C
G
C
make one at the bot - tom of the deep blue sea!

SHERLOCK'S CASE NOTES

- *The children can fold their arms and move them side to side as if dancing a sailor's hornpipe on the first two verses as they sing "Down, down" etc.*
- *Beware the change of words after the first verse – only verse 1 should be "Down, down,* ***to*** *the bottom of the sea", subsequent verses are all "Down, down* ***at*** *the bottom of the sea".*
- *The words in the verses need to be very clear. Ask the children to whisper the words with exaggerated mouth movements so that they move their tongue and lips, or chant or sing the words with a character voice (pirate, Dalek, cartoon character etc).*
- *The ending of the song from bars 26 onwards "For in fairy tales ev'ry wish comes true" will need extra care, as initially the children will sing the familiar tune rather than the one written.*
- *Adding actions to the phrases "seaweed waves and dolphins play" and "the crab and lobster hide away" (bar 11 onwards) will help the children to learn the words.*

Singing Sherlock wants to know:

- *Are you managing to perform all your actions together as well as singing your words clearly for "seaweed waves and dolphins play" and "the crab and lobster hide away"?*
- *Are you remembering the different ending after you have sung the third verse?*
- *Can you sound amazed and excited when you sing the words "for he'd turned into a real live boy"?*

The End!